635

R.J.H.Miller,
111 Ashbourne Drive,
Islington, Ontario

May 1962

biochemical mechanisms

biochemical mechanisms

John Wiley & Sons, Inc., New York • London

LLOYD L. INGRAHAM

Department of Biochemistry and Biophysics
University of California, Davis, California

GENERAL PUBLISHING CO. LTD.
222 ADELAIDE ST. W.
TORONTO

"It is quite natural that enzyme chemists have, thus far, been occupied with the discovery of many kinds of enzymes, the ingenious methods of preparing them, and the measurement of their activity. But at this point we must inquire into the chemical mechanism by which they work."

L. Michaelis 1946

preface

Biochemistry has now reached a stage in its development that requires a knowledge of mechanistic chemical principles. Many excellent books are available which contain this background material, but these often do not fill the special needs of the biochemist. Acidity functions in strong acid solution, for example, are of no interest in the study of reactions at physiological pH values.

The use of structure variations to determine mechanisms is explained fully in books dealing with physical organic chemistry. This method has been extremely valuable in understanding organic mechanisms, but is of less value to the biochemist who deals with enzymes with great substrate specificities.

Biochemical mechanisms are a specialized branch of mechanistic chemistry. Enzyme reactions occur through transition states that are held in very definite fixed positions. This allows mechanisms that are less likely in usual solution chemistry. Acidic and basic catalysts such as carboxyl groups and amino groups are available at exactly the correct position; therefore the entropy of activation is of less hindrance in enzymic reactions than in solution chemistry. In addition the biochemist is interested in inorganic as well as organic mechanisms, and the two must be correlated. Finally the biochemist wants concrete examples of mechanisms in biochemical systems, and the methods that were used to determine these mechanisms. These specialized problems require a specialized book on biochemical mechanisms, which I have tried to provide.

The book is divided into two parts. The first part reviews general mechanistic principles of organic and inorganic chemistry that are of value to biochemistry. This includes a review of orbital and other fairly basic concepts in order to facilitate the discussion of mechanisms in the second section.

The second part treats specific biochemical mechanisms. This part is divided into various type reactions. The mechanism of the reaction as known in solution chemistry is discussed in terms of principles that may apply to the biochemical reaction. Next the mechanisms of action of any model enzymes are described, and finally the enzymic reaction is compared with model reactions.

No attempt is made to include the mechanisms of purely physiological processes such as absorption, secretion, muscle contraction, or nerve action. Our knowledge has not advanced to a state where it seems possible to explain these processes from a reaction mechanism point of view. The reader should be warned that many of the mechanisms given in this book are highly speculative. Any book on biochemical mechanisms would necessarily be so at this date. The purpose in speculating on mechanisms is only to encourage research; mechanisms should not gain in stature merely because they are in print.

I wish to acknowledge the inspiration of F. H. Westheimer. Dr. Westheimer has so many ideas that after spending a year with him it is difficult to give specific credit to those here which are rightfully his.

I wish to thank my wife, Marie Ingraham, for proofreading and repeated retypings of the manuscript.

LLOYD L. INGRAHAM

Davis, California
November, 1961

contents

ix

part one

ATOMIC ORBITALS

Electrons have the interesting characteristic of showing the properties of both particles and waves. The fact that electrons may be considered as standing waves in a potential field means that they may only have certain frequencies or energies in a given potential field. A guitar string, for example, may vibrate with a given frequency or energy and harmonics of this frequency but is not allowed to vibrate at frequencies at random. This restriction on energy means that the electrons around a nucleus must exist in definite energy levels.

The wave motion of an electron can be expressed by the wave equation

$$\frac{\partial^2 \psi}{\partial x^2} + \frac{\partial^2 \psi}{\partial y^2} + \frac{\partial^2 \psi}{\partial z^2} + \frac{8\pi^2 m}{h^2}(E - V)\psi = 0$$

which relates the amplitude ψ of the waves at any position (x, y, z) to the mass of the electron m, the total energy of the electron E, and the potential energy V. The symbol h is Planck's constant. This is a differential equation, and solutions of amplitude ψ as a function of x, y, and z are possible for only certain values of E, which is the mathematical reason for the restrictions in energy levels. If we consider an electron in a hydrogen atom, V is the coulombic potential energy between the positively charged nucleus and the electron. Many solutions are possible for the equation describing an electron in a hydrogen atom, but all may be summarized in a rather complex general solution in terms of the coordinates, several constants, and three numbers n, l, and m. The particular solutions are obtained by substituting certain integral values for n, l, and m. Not all values are possible, and the values used for one constant depend on the value given to the other constant. These constants are called quantum numbers. The *principal* quantum number, n, determines the size of the orbit; the *orbital* quantum number, l, determines the shape of the orbit; and the *magnetic* quantum number, m, determines the special orientation of the orbit. In addition, the electron itself has a magnetic spin of $\frac{1}{2}$ or $-\frac{1}{2}$ of a Bohr magneton depending upon its orientation, measured by the spin quantum number s. The four quantum numbers, n, l, m, and s completely describe an electron.

No two electrons in the same atom can have the same values for these four quantum numbers. The principal quantum number, n, can have positive integral values 1, 2, 3, 4, etc. The orbital quantum number, l, can have integral values including zero between zero and $n - 1$. The magnetic quantum number, m, can have both positive and negative values, including zero, between and including $-l$ and l. The spin quantum number, s, can have only values of $\pm\frac{1}{2}$. The quantum numbers of the ten electrons in the $n = 1$ and $n = 2$ levels are shown below. Notice that no two electrons have the same four quantum numbers.

n	l	m	s	Designation
1	0	0	$\frac{1}{2}$	$1s$
1	0	0	$-\frac{1}{2}$	$1s$
2	0	0	$\frac{1}{2}$	$2s$
2	0	0	$-\frac{1}{2}$	$2s$
2	1	-1	$\frac{1}{2}$	$2p$
2	1	-1	$-\frac{1}{2}$	$2p$
2	1	0	$\frac{1}{2}$	$2p$
2	1	0	$-\frac{1}{2}$	$2p$
2	1	1	$\frac{1}{2}$	$2p$
2	1	1	$-\frac{1}{2}$	$2p$

An orbital is described by the quantum numbers n, l, and m, so that an orbital may contain two electrons, one with $s = \frac{1}{2}$ and the other with $s = -\frac{1}{2}$. Orbitals with $l = 0, 1, 2, 3$ and 4, are designated by the symbols s, p, d, f and g, respectively. After f the letters are in alphabetical order. A $2s$ orbital means $n = 2$ and $l = 0$, and a $4p$ orbital means $p = 4$ and $l = 1$. From the table above it is evident that there is only one $1s$ orbital and only one $2s$ orbital but there are three $2p$ orbitals. Further extrapolation will show that there are five $3d$ orbitals. All of these orbitals (s, p, d, f, g, etc.) are solutions of the wave equation and determine the amplitude of the wave at any position. No physical meaning can be attached to the orbital other than the concept of wave amplitude. Nevertheless, orbitals are a valuable concept that will prove useful in later discussions of enzyme mechanisms. The value of the orbital varies with the direction and distance from the nucleus. The equations for two typical wave functions or orbitals are shown below:

n	l	m	Orbital

$$1 \quad 0 \quad 0 \qquad \psi_{1s} = \frac{1}{\sqrt{\pi}}\left(\frac{Z}{a_0}\right)^{3/2} e^{-\rho}$$

$$2 \quad 1 \quad 0 \qquad \psi_{2pz} = \frac{1}{4\sqrt{2\pi}}\left(\frac{Z}{a_0}\right)^{3/2} \rho e^{-\rho/2} \cos\theta$$

The symbol Z stands for the nuclear charge, a_0 is a constant, and $\rho = r/a_0$.

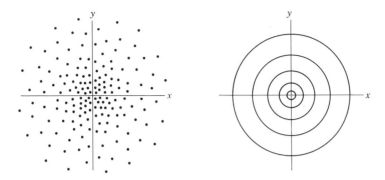

The coordinates r, θ, and ϕ are the usual three-dimensional polar co-ordinates. Some of the other orbitals, for example ψ_{2pz}, depend upon ϕ. Notice that the $1s$ orbital depends only on r and not θ so that it is spheri-cally symmetrical. The $2pz$ orbital depends on θ, so that this orbital is not spherically symmetrical. The orbitals are continuous functions of r, θ, and ϕ, and have values at all positions in space. The amplitude of a $1s$ orbital decreases with distance from the nucleus so that it should be described in the xy plane either by a density of dots or by contour lines. However, orbitals are usually plotted as sliced in one plane and only showing one of the contours. This type of plot is shown below for various orbitals. Orbitals are not hollow spheres as these diagrams would indicate but are

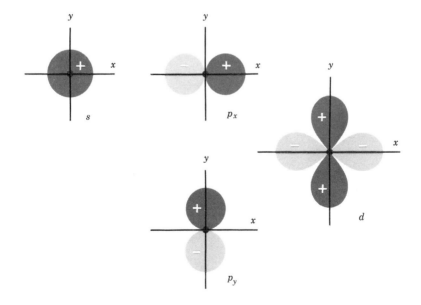

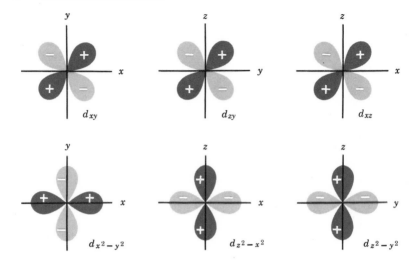

actually diffuse three-dimensional structures which only gradually decrease in value through space.

The $2s$ orbitals are all positive and symmetrical with respect to the atomic nucleus, whereas the three $2p$ orbitals contain positive and negative lobes along the three axes, x, y, and z. These orbitals may be designated $2p_x$, $2p_y$, and $2p_z$. The d orbitals have two positive lobes and two negative lobes. The d orbitals with lobes diagonally between the axis are called d_{xy}, d_{yz}, and d_{xz} respectively. The d orbitals with lobes on the axis are called $d_{x^2-y^2}$, $d_{z^2-x^2}$, and $d_{z^2-y^2}$ respectively. Theory predicted only five independent $3d$ orbitals and six have been described above. The answer is that only five are independent. The relationship

$$d_{z^2-y^2} - d_{x^2-y^2} = d_{z^2-x^2}$$

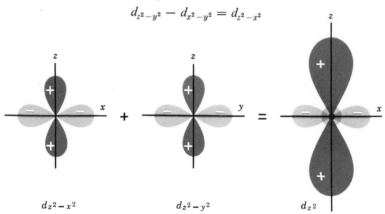

shows that the last three are linearly dependent. Usually a new orbital called d_{z^2} is formed by adding $d_{z^2-y^2}$ and $d_{z^2-x^2}$. The five orbitals are then taken as d_{xy}, d_{yz}, d_{xz}, $d_{x^2-y^2}$, and d_{z^2}. The signs of the orbitals refer only to the sign of the amplitude of the wave functions, and are not related to the spin or electron density. The n quantum number changes the sign of the orbital and the internal structure but not the shape, for example, 2s orbitals are larger than 1s orbitals and contain a nodal sphere of zero amplitude. The sign of the amplitude changes at this node.

The easiest way to show this is by a plot of the amplitude against the distance, d, from the nucleus. Similar changes in internal structure occur

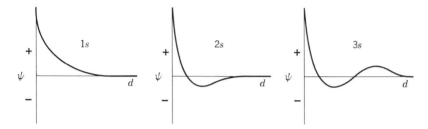

with the higher p and d orbitals. Differences in internal structure, however, are not of importance in the qualitative descriptions of chemical reactions, so that internal structure will be neglected in further discussions.

The square of the orbital does have physical meaning: in any small area

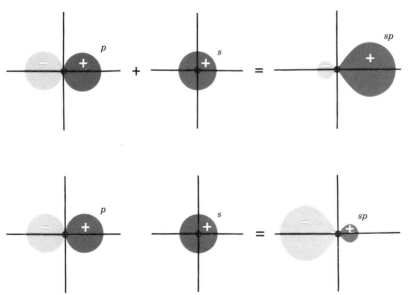

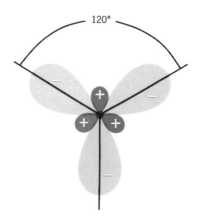

it measures the electron density or the portion of the electron existing in that small area. The electrons are smeared throughout the orbital. The electron density is always positive because the square of the orbital will always be positive.

A new function may be formed by adding the two solutions, $2s$ and $2p$, of the wave equation. This new function satisfies the wave equation and is therefore an orbital. It satisfies the wave equation because linear combinations of solutions of a differential equation are also solutions of the equation. These new orbitals, formed by adding and subtracting $2s$ and $2p$ orbitals, are called hybridized orbitals and are designated as sp orbitals. Notice that they are oriented at 180° to each other. The two unhybridized p orbitals are perpendicular to these orbitals and perpendicular to each other. Linear combinations of one s with two p orbitals are similarly called sp^2 orbitals. The maximum extensions of these orbitals are in a plane oriented at 120° to each other. The unhybridized p orbital is perpendicular to the plane formed by the three sp^2 orbitals. Linear combinations of an s with all three p orbitals form four new sp^3 hybrid orbitals oriented at 109° to each other. The individual sp^3 orbitals appear much like the individual sp^2 orbitals.

BONDING

When atoms are close enough for the atomic orbitals to interact, a new orbital is formed. This may be approximated by linear combinations of the two atomic orbitals, because linear combination of atomic orbitals on different atoms are approximate solutions of the molecular wave equation. The wave equation which gave the atomic orbital, however, considered

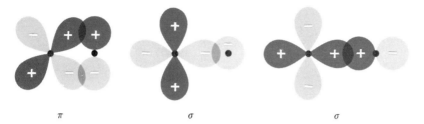

π σ σ

only a single point charge at the nucleus of the atom and the wave equation for a diatomic molecule must consider two point positive charges. Clearly, the wave equation for an atom is not the same for a diatomic molecule, and the sum or difference of two atomic orbitals should not give a solution to the molecular wave equation. This approximation, however, is commonly made because of the difficulty in solving the molecular wave equation. Orbitals formed by the addition of atomic orbitals are called molecular

orbitals and are given quantum numbers corresponding to the atomic quantum numbers. Molecular orbital quantum number, λ, corresponds to l, and takes values 0, 1, 2, etc. called σ, π, δ, etc. corresponding to s, p, d, etc. Corresponding to the symmetrical s atomic orbitals, σ orbitals are symmetrical about a line joining the two atoms. Similarily, π molecular orbitals are unsymmetrical about a line joining the two atoms, corresponding to the unsymmetrical p atomic orbitals. Bonds formed from p orbitals at other angles are called σ, π hybrids.

$2p$ $2s$

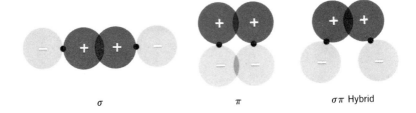

σ   π   σπ Hybrid

Side views

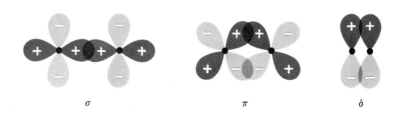

σ   π   δ

End views

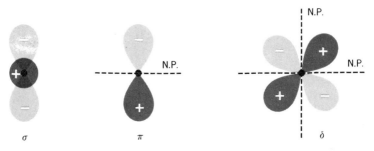

σ   π   δ

N.P. = nodal plane

Oblique view

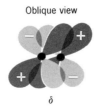

δ

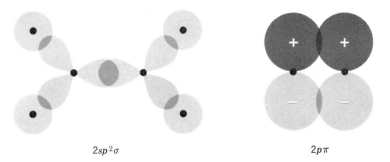

$2sp^2\sigma$ $2p\pi$

Similar bonds may be formed from d orbitals, which may overlap to form σ bonds, π bonds, or δ bonds. The π bonds are unsymmetrical about one plane, as was true for π bonds formed from p orbitals, but the δ bonds have two nodal planes containing the line between the atoms. The latter, δ bonds, are uncommon; they occur in bonds between two metals. These d orbitals may also form bonds with s and p orbitals.

Because the d_{xy}, d_{yz}, and d_{xz} can form π bonds these are commonly called the d_π atomic orbitals. Similarly $d_{x^2-y^2}$ and d_{z^2} are called d_σ orbitals.

Because the shapes of orbitals are diffuse the overlap areas are diffuse also. Positive lobes of atomic orbitals will add to positive lobes they overlap and negative lobes will add to negative lobes giving a new molecular orbital. However, positive lobes will only subtract from negative lobes and there will be no bond. The difference of two p orbitals oriented in the same manner, the mathematical equivalent of the sum of two p orbitals oriented in oppositive directions, will cause repulsion between the atoms. Similarly a $2s$ orbital will not bond with a $2p$ orbital when placed as shown below, because although the positive-positive overlap adds, the positive-negative subtracts. The repulsion caused by the subtraction and the attraction caused by the addition give a new result of no interaction between these two orbitals in this position.

Methane and other saturated hydrocarbons are made up of sp^3 orbitals of carbon with the hydrogens all at $109°$ to each other. In ethylene the sp^2 orbitals of the two carbons overlap to make a $sp^2\sigma$ bond between the carbon atoms, and the unhybridized p orbitals, perpendicular to the sp^2 orbitals, overlap to form a $2p\pi$ bond. The double bond of ethylene is therefore composed of one $2sp^2\sigma$ bond and one $2p\pi$ bond.

CONJUGATED SYSTEMS

Carrying this approximation to butadiene brings about a very interesting situation. The orbitals may now overlap on both sides to make a very

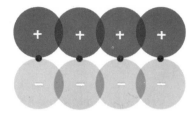

stable π orbital. However, this orbital can only contain two electrons and we have four p electrons in butadiene. An orbital with repulsion between the center carbons contains the other two electrons. Because of this peculiar property of p orbitals to overlap on two sides at once certain conjugated molecules are more stable, and do not have the properties that would be expected if this effect had not been considered. Carbon may in effect, therefore, form more than four bonds if the p orbitals are properly oriented. The carbons in benzene each form 4.33 bonds[1] and this extra bonding makes benzene more stable than the Kekule structure would indicate.

LIGAND FIELD THEORY[2]

In a free ion all of the five d orbitals have the same energy level. However, in a chelate or complex some of the filled orbitals are oriented toward the chelating atoms. Repulsion between nonbonding electrons in the d orbital and those on the chelating atom causes electrons in these orbitals to be less stable with respect to the other orbitals. In addition, bonding can preferentially stabilize one orbital with respect to the others. The theory dealing with repulsions from the field produced by the chelating atoms is called crystal field theory; the total effects are dealt with in ligand field theory.

Crystal field theory will be discussed first. The splittings produced in the d orbitals depend on the type of field. Notice, for example, that the d_{z^2} orbital becomes less stable in a octahedral field because of the atom on the z axis, but more stable in a square planar field because there is no atom at the z axis.

[1] C. A. Coulson, *J. chim. phys.* **45**, 243–8 (1948)

[2] F. Basolo and R. G. Pearson, *Mechanisms of Inorganic Reactions*, John Wiley and Sons, Inc., New York (1958); L. E. Orgel, *An Introduction to Transition-Metal Chemistry—Ligand Field Theory*, John Wiley and Sons, Inc., New York (1960)
The author wishes to acknowledge the aid of C. H. Burke in wording portions of this section.

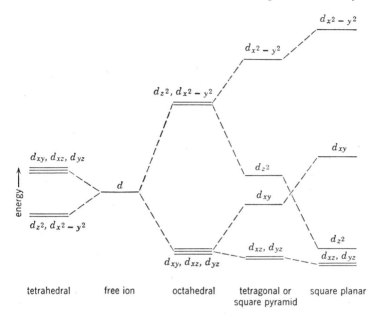

tetrahedral   free ion   octahedral   tetragonal or   square planar
square pyramid

Consider a tetrahedral field. If the central ion occupies the exact center of the box and the ligands four of the corners, then the symmetry of a tetrahedral complex can be shown schematically as by the following diagram.

This diagram makes apparent that the lobes of the d_{xy}, d_{xz}, and d_{yz} orbitals are near the ligands. The lobes of the $d_{x^2-y^2}$ and d_{z^2} orbitals lie on angles between the pairs of ligands. Consequently, the $d_{x^2-y^2}$ and d_{z^2} orbitals are repelled much less by the ligands than are the d_{xy}, d_{xz}, and d_{yz}

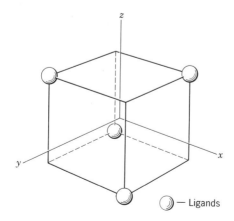

◯ — Ligands

orbitals. This explains why the d_{xy}, d_{xz}, and d_{yz} orbitals are split to higher energy levels than are the other two orbitals when in the tetrahedral configuration.

Splitting, which occurs when the symmetry of the ligands about the central ion is the octahedral configuration, is the reverse of that seen in the tetrahedral configuration. In octahedral field splitting the d_{z^2} and $d_{x^2-y^2}$ orbitals are repelled more by the ligands and consequently split to higher energy levels than are the d_{xy}, d_{xz}, and d_{yz} orbitals.

By preferentially filling the low energy orbitals, the d orbitals can stabilize the system. For example, if three orbitals have a low energy and two have a higher energy, as in an octahedral complex, the configuration would be much more stable with six electrons occupying the low energy levels, than with the electrons spread through all five orbitals. The gain in bonding energy achieved in this manner is referred to as the crystal field stabilization energy (CFSE).

Complexes with more of the electrons in the lower energy levels are more stable than those with all of the d orbitals equally filled. Trivalent chromium and cobalt, for example, with three and six electrons respectively, will form very stable complexes or ions. This is because when a chelate is formed and the orbitals are split, the electrons can all be accommodated in the three low d orbitals. Consequently, the tendency of these ions to form complexes is very great. A complex of univalent copper, on the other hand, has zero CFSE because the five orbitals are completely filled. As a result, cuprous complexes will be less stable than those of trivalent cobalt or trivalent chromium.

Crystal field effects are important in predicting the rates and mechanisms of reactions of coordination compounds. The essential feature here is that ions which are strongly crystal field stabilized will be slow to react. Nonstabilized ions will be more labile. This explains why cobalt (III), which has considerable CFSE, is so nonreactive. In order for cobalt (III) to react, the octahedral configuration, which creates the large CFSE, must first be disrupted.

Crystal field theory makes possible correlations between redox potentials. Since the CFSE of cupric ion complexes is six times that of cuprous ion complexes, oxidation of the cuprous ion should be easy. Conversely, ferrous ion complexed with *o*-phenanthroline, which has a large crystal field and creates a very stable orbital occupied by the electron, is oxidized to the ferric state only with difficulty. If ferrous ion is complexed with water or carboxylate-type ligands of low crystal field strengths, oxidation to the ferric state will be easier, as the electron will be taken from a less stabilized orbital.

The colors of most transition metal complexes, for example, cupric blue, are due to transitions of an electron from a low d orbital to a higher unoccupied d orbital. Crystal field stabilization energies may be calculated from the observed spectra.

The second effect, bonding, is usually considered as a correction to the electrostatic effects discussed above.

In considering the crystal field strengths of any set of ligands, it is difficult to class the ligands in order of crystal field strengths in terms of electrostatic factors only. Ligands which produce the greatest amount of splitting in metal ions form complexes of greatest stability. In octahedral complexes of a number of transition ions, spectral evidence reveals an order of decreasing crystal field strength for the ligands: $CN^- > o$-phenanthroline $> NO_2^- >$ ethylenediamine $>$ ammonia $> SCN^- > H_2O > F^- > COO^- > OH^- > Cl^- > Br^-$. However, o-phenanthroline does not produce a more intense electric field than does fluoride ion, nor does water produce a stronger electric field than does hydroxide ion. Yet, as just mentioned, in octahedral complexes of several transition ions, o-phenanthroline and water are listed as ligands having a stronger crystal field strength than either fluoride or hydroxide ions. Such discrepancies can be accounted for by assuming that certain ligands with p orbitals can form $dp\pi$ bonds with the metal ion and thus help stabilize the d_π orbitals. To account for these covalency effects some workers have proposed that the name "ligand field theory" be used for the combined approach. As a result, crystal field, or ligand field splittings, are now interpreted as being partly due to electrostatic forces and partly due to covalent bond formation. The greater crystal field splittings of o-phenanthroline as compared with fluoride ion would be explained then by this combined approach.

TRANSITION STATES

The expression for an equilibrium constant should contain activities instead of concentrations. One might be inclined also to write the rate of a

$$A + B \rightleftharpoons C + D$$

$$K = \frac{(a_C)(a_D)}{(a_A)(a_B)} = \frac{(C)\gamma_C(D)\gamma_D}{(A)\gamma_A(B)\gamma_B}$$

reaction as proportional to the activities of the reactants, where the symbol a_A is the activity of A, (A) is the concentration of A, γ_A is the activity coefficient of A, and analogous symbols apply for B. Equation I would

$$A + B \xrightarrow{k} \quad -\frac{d(A)}{dt} = k(a_A)(a_B) = k(A)\gamma_A(B)\gamma_B \qquad \text{False!} \qquad \text{I}$$

predict, because activity coefficients decrease upon an increase in ionic strength, that rates of chemical reactions would decrease upon an increase in ionic strength. However, the reaction of $[Co(NH_3)_5Br]^{2+}$ with Hg^{2+} to form $[Co(NH_3)_5H_2O]^{3+}$ increases in rate with an increase in ionic strength of the solution. This and many other examples of reactions between ions of the same charge show that the simple rate equation I is false.[3] The problem is most simply solved by assuming the existence of an activated complex or transition state between reactants and products. The reactants are in equilibrium with the transition state and the rate of product formation is proportional to the concentration of the transition state.

$$A + B \underset{}{\overset{K^{\ddagger}}{\rightleftharpoons}} AB^{\ddagger} \xrightarrow{k'} C + D$$

$$K^{\ddagger} = \frac{(AB^{\ddagger})\gamma^{\ddagger}}{(A)\gamma_A(B)\gamma_B}$$

The concentration of the transition state is measured by the equilibrium constant $K^{\ddagger}$, where γ_A, γ_B, and $\gamma^{\ddagger}$ are the activity coefficients for A, B, and $AB^{\ddagger}$, respectively. Solving for $(AB^{\ddagger})$ gives

$$(AB^{\ddagger}) = \frac{K^{\ddagger}(A)\gamma_A(B)\gamma_B}{\gamma^{\ddagger}}$$

If we set the rate of formation of product C, $\dfrac{d(C)}{dt} = k'(AB^{\ddagger})$ substitution for $(AB^{\ddagger})$ gives

$$\frac{d(C)}{dt} = \frac{k'K^{\ddagger}(A)\gamma_A(B)\gamma_B}{\gamma^{\ddagger}} \qquad \text{II}$$

or

$$\frac{d(C)}{dt} = \frac{k(A)\gamma_A(B)\gamma_B}{\gamma^{\ddagger}}$$

where $k'K^{\ddagger} = k$. Inspection of equation II shows that if $\gamma^{\ddagger}$ decreases more than the product $\gamma_A\gamma_B$ on the addition of salt the rate will increase, whereas if $\gamma_A\gamma_B$ decreases more than $\gamma^{\ddagger}$ on the addition of salt the rate will decrease. The first situation arises when both ions have the same charge. The transition state will therefore have a double charge, and, according to the Debye-Huckel theory which states that the logarithm of the activity coefficient depends on both the ionic strength and the square of the charge on the ion, the product $\gamma_A\gamma_B$ will decrease less than $\gamma^{\ddagger}$ when salt is added. The assumption of an intermediate transition state which leads to equation II therefore explains why rates can either increase or decrease when salt is added, whereas activity coefficients always decrease.

[3] J. N. Bronsted and R. Livingston, *J. Am. Chem. Soc.* **49**, 435 (1927)

The transition state is defined as the configuration of the reactants (or products) when the potential energy of the system is a maximum. The structure of this transition state is extremely important in the discussion of any rates because the rate constant depends on the equilibrium constant $K^{\ddagger}$, which is a measure of the relative stabilities of the reactants and the transition state.

In addition, the activity coefficient of the transition state, $\gamma^{\ddagger}$, affects the overall rate of reaction. Catalysts, including enzymes, also increase $K^{\ddagger}$; a secondary effect may be to decrease $\gamma^{\ddagger}$. The free energy difference between reactants and the transition state is called the free energy of activation.

$$\Delta F^{\ddagger} = -RT \ln K^{\ddagger}$$

The free energy of activation, $\Delta F^{\ddagger}$, like the usual free energies, is composed of an entropy of activation and a heat of activation.

$$\Delta F^{\ddagger} = \Delta H^{\ddagger} - T \Delta S^{\ddagger}$$

An enzyme may increase $K^{\ddagger}$ and hence the rate of reaction by decreasing $\Delta H^{\ddagger}$ or increasing $\Delta S^{\ddagger}$. The purpose of this book is to discuss mechanisms by which this may be accomplished.

Although most of the discussion will be concerned with decreasing the $\Delta H^{\ddagger}$ term, an important function of enzymes is to increase the $\Delta S^{\ddagger}$ term by holding the reactants in the proper position for reaction. Enzymic reactions are characterized by a more positive entropy of activation because the reactants are held fairly rigidly before the transition state is reached. If the reactants were in random positions there would be a large decrease in entropy in order to form a transition state and the entropy of activation would have a large negative value. An important function of metals in enzymes[4] may be to aid in the gathering process and increase the entropy of activation. The unfavorable entropy in the gathering up process does not concern our discussion of rates because this is not the rate-determining step. Manganous ion has been shown to be important in binding substrate to enzyme in the enolase reaction.[5] The importance of the $\Delta S^{\ddagger}$ term in enzyme-catalyzed reactions is demonstrated by pepsin. The pepsin-catalyzed hydrolysis of carbobenzoxy glutamyl tyrosine has a heat of activation[6] of 23.1 $\pm$ 1.2 kcal, comparable with that found for the acid-catalyzed hydrolysis of peptides, 19.7 kcal. However, the entropy of activation (starting with free enzyme and free substrate) is 16.1 e.u. for the enzyme and -16.6 e.u. to -27.1 e.u. for hydrolyse acid-catalyzed peptides.[7]

[4] L. L. Ingraham and D. E. Green, *Science* **128**, 310 (1958)
[5] B. G. Malmstrom, T. Vanngard, and M. Larsson, *Biochim. et Biophys. Acta* **30**, 1 (1958)
[6] E. J. Casey and K. J. Laidler, *J. Am. Chem. Soc.* **72**, 2159 (1950)
[7] L. Lawrence and E. J. Moore, *J. Am. Chem. Soc.* **73**, 3973 (1951)

Often discussions of enzymes mechanisms state that the enzyme may act by straining the substrate so that reaction occurs more easily. This merely means that the enzyme-substrate complex is farther up on the side of the $\Delta F^{\ddagger}$ barrier. The reaction rate is determined only by the $\Delta F^{\ddagger}$, the difference between the transition state and the initial state. Unless the strain in the initial reactants is of the type that preferentially stabilizes the transition state, as, for example, in the Smiles rearrangement,[8] strain will not increase the rate of reaction. In general, statements that enzymes catalyze reactions by straining the substrate are not true. Attention should be focused on the stability of the transition state instead of strain.

IONIC REACTIONS

If the bond is broken so that the two electrons both remain on one atom, this atom will have an excess of electrons whereas the other atom will have an electron deficiency and ions will be formed. We are so accustomed to ions in aqueous solution that it is difficult to imagine how difficult they are to form unless they are stabilized in some manner. In the gas phase, even a material as ionic as sodium chloride will dissociate into sodium and chlorine atoms upon heating. However, water is quite polar and the water molecules clustered about the ions in aqueous solution amount to large stabilization energies so that hydration energy is an important concept when ionic mechanisms are discussed.

Ions with a positive charge on carbon are called carbonium ions and ions with a negative charge on carbon are called carbanions. Because the $2s$ orbitals lie at a lower energy level than the $2p$ orbitals, the six electrons around a carbonium ion are in the $2s$ and two of the $2p$ orbitals. The hybridization of the bonds is therefore sp^2 instead of sp^3 and the bonds are

$2s$	$2p$		$2s$	$2p$	
	oo *oo*			*oo* *oo* *oo*	
oo			*oo*		
Carbonium Ion			Carbanion		
sp^2			sp^3		

all planar. A carbonium ion may react on either side with another reagent so that an optically active compound will form a D and L racemic mixture of products if the reaction proceeds via a carbonium ion intermediate. Such reactions are unimolecular because the ionization to form the carbonium ion is rate determining. The rate of reaction of the carbonium

---

[8] J. F. Bunnett and T. Okamoto, *J. Am. Chem. Soc.* **78**, 5363 (1956)

ion with solvent or a nucleophile is relatively fast. These reactions are called S_N1, meaning substitution nucleophilic unimolecular. Carbanions on the other hand are tetrahedral because the $2s$ and all $2p$ orbitals are filled with eight electrons now present.

DISPLACEMENT REACTIONS

The displacement reaction is a reaction in which a new bond is formed simultaneously as the old bond is broken. The partial formation of a new bond helps to stabilize the transition state[9] and hastens the reaction: so the displacement reaction is thus an important basic mechanism for obtaining a rapid reaction. The importance of displacement reactions in biochemical mechanisms has been pointed out by Koshland.[10]

Displacement reactions may be of three types, nucleophilic, electrophilic, and radical. In nucleophilic displacements the attacking group carries a

$$X: + \underset{R_3}{C:Y} \longrightarrow \underset{R_3}{X:C} + :Y$$

pair of electrons, and the leaving group Y leaves with a pair. In electrophilic displacement X does not have an available pair of electrons and Y

$$X + \underset{R_3}{Y:C} \longrightarrow \underset{R_3}{X:C} + Y$$

leaves without a pair. Radical displacements are those in which X carries one electron and Y leaves with one electron.

$$X\cdot + \underset{R_3}{C:Y} \longrightarrow \underset{R_3}{X:C} + Y\cdot$$

The reasons for the efficiency of a nucleophilic displacement reaction are best appreciated from a knowledge of the detailed mechanism.[11] When the reactant X attacks the carbon of the R_3CY, the orbital of the reagent X begins to overlap the rear lobe of the sp^3 orbital on carbon, bonding the Y groups, and the rear lobe gradually expands until the sp^3 orbital becomes a pure p orbital. The C—R bonds now become sp^2, and the CR_3 group becomes planar. At this stage the CR_3 group has the character of a carbonium ion and the p orbital is capable of doing double duty by partially

[9] E. D. Hughes and C. K. Ingold, *J. Chem. Soc.* **1935**, 244

[10] D. E. Koshland, Jr., *J. Am. Chem. Soc.* **74**, 2286 (1952); D. E. Koshland, Jr., *The Mechanism of Enzyme Action*, edited by W. D. McElroy and B. Glass, Johns Hopkins Press (1954), p. 608; D. E. Koshland, Jr., *Biol. Rev.* **28**, 416 (1953)

[11] A. Streitweiser, Jr., *Chem. Rev.* **56**, 571 (1956)

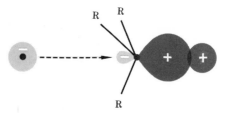

bonding with one lobe to the X and partially with the other to the Y. This extra bonding stabilizes the transition state, makes $K^{\ddagger}$ large, and causes the reaction to be fast. The reaction sequence in terms of orbitals therefore proceeds as shown below:

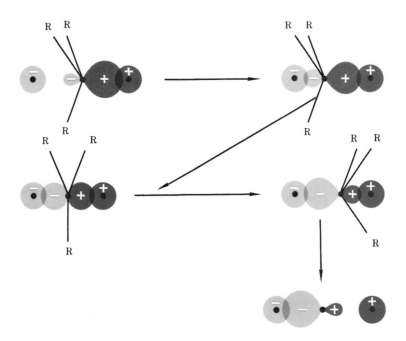

   Bimolecular nucleophilic displacement reactions are an important fundamental mechanism which occur in many reactions. They are called S_N2, standing for substitution nucleophilic bimolecular. The attack by X must be to the rear of the Y so that the optical activity of the product is inverted. Because the attack is on the rear of the carbon, the size of the R groups greatly affects the rate of reaction. Large R groups slow down the reaction. Nucleophilic displacement reactions occur much faster on primary carbon atoms than on more highly substituted carbon atoms.

The reagent X: carrying the pair of electrons is called a nucleophilic reagent and the relative rate of reaction of the nucleophilic reagent is called the nucleophilicity of the reagent. Because a proton may share the pair of electrons on the nucleophilic reagent, they are commonly bases.

$$X: + H^+ \rightleftharpoons X:H^+$$

and one might expect that the stronger the base (the more available the electrons), the better will be the nucleophile. This is not entirely true because nucleophilicity also depends on the relative polarizability of the atom, so that often the comparative rates of reaction of a series of X: in displacement reactions are not quantitatively related to their basicity. Polarizable atoms have stretchable bonds and thus may more readily form long partial bonds to the central atom in the transition state and stabilize the transition state by this extra amount of bonding. The atoms of higher

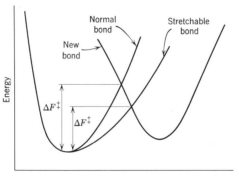

atomic weight in a given group are more polarizable than those of lower molecular weight. Sulfur is a very polarizable atom and sulfur compounds are very good nucleophilic reagents; they are quite common enzymic catalysts, for example, in glutathione and coenzyme A. Nitrogen bases and in particular imidazoles are better nucleophiles than would be expected from their basicity,[12] which helps to explain why histidine may be so important in the functioning of the esterases.

Miller and Parker[13] have minimized the effect of polarizability on the nucleophilicity of large atoms, and have stressed the lack of solvation which causes them to be better nucleophiles. Perhaps both effects are important. Regardless of cause, large atoms are good nucleophiles.

The structure of the leaving group :X also determines the rate of a

---

[12] T. C. Bruice and R. Lapinski, *J. Am. Chem. Soc.* **80**, 2265 (1958)
[13] L. Miller and A. L. Parker, *J. Am. Chem. Soc.* **83**, 117 (1961); A. L. Parker, *J. Chem. Soc.* **1961**, 1328

nucleophilic displacement reaction. The ability of a group to leave depends on the ability to accommodate a negative charge and the polarizability. To accommodate a negative charge, the group should be a weak base or the anion of a strong acid. Polarizable atoms like sulfur and iodine are not only good attacking groups but also good leaving groups. Good leaving groups in biological systems are phosphate ion because it is the anion of a strong acid and coenzyme A because of the polarizable sulfur atom.

Often two successive displacement reactions, called a double displacement reaction, will have a faster rate than a single displacement reaction. If a very polarizable atom displaces a group and an entering group displaces the polarizable atom, a double displacement reaction occurs in which each step has a lower activation energy than the single displacement. Double

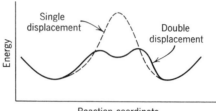

Reaction coordinate

displacement reactions probably occur in enzyme reactions with a group on the enzyme serving as the polarizable group.

Electrophilic displacement reactions take place with retention of configuration, because the transition state has characteristics of a tetrahedral carbanion. The central carbon atom is now sp^3, so that the orbital of the entering group is unable to overlap with the other lobe of a p orbital as in the nucleophilic substitution, but now must overlap with the same lobe as the leaving group does. The mechanism of an electrophilic reaction in terms of orbitals must therefore proceed as follows:

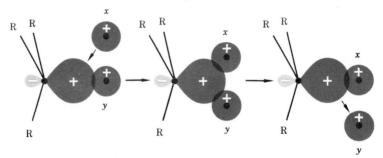

Winstein and Traylor point out that because both the entering and leaving groups are deficient in electrons, electron sharing between them will stabilize the transition state that leads to retention of configuration.[14] Retention of configuration has been experimentally demonstrated by the following reaction:

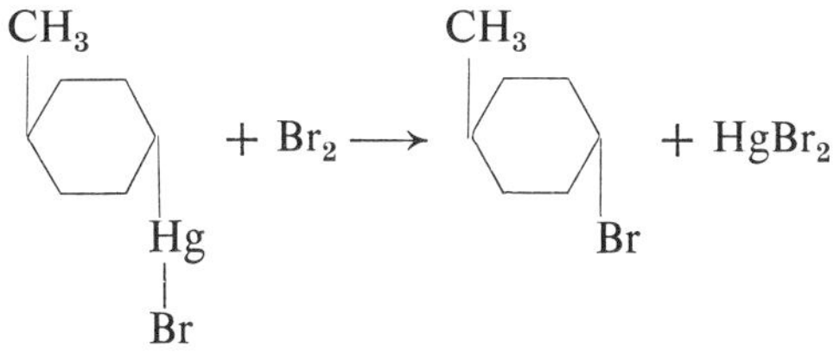

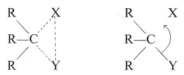

$$\text{(toluene-Hg-Br)} + Br_2 \longrightarrow \text{(toluene-Br)} + HgBr_2$$

Electrophilic displacement reactions are commonly written with a dashed triangle or a curved arrow.

Electrophilic displacement reactions commonly occur in reactions of aromatic compounds; for example, the bromination of benzene by Br^+ and the nitration of benzene by $NO_2{}^+$ are electrophilic displacement reactions. However, the mechanism of aromatic electrophilic substitution[14] reactions differs from that of aliphatic reactions. The experimental fact that no tritium rate effect is found in aromatic nitration is not consistent with a simple displacement reaction as proposed for the aliphatic mechanism but is consistent with a two-step reaction proceeding by way of a fairly stable intermediate ion. For example, the residual paratritiotoluene after nitration is not enriched in tritium. This result can be explained if the first

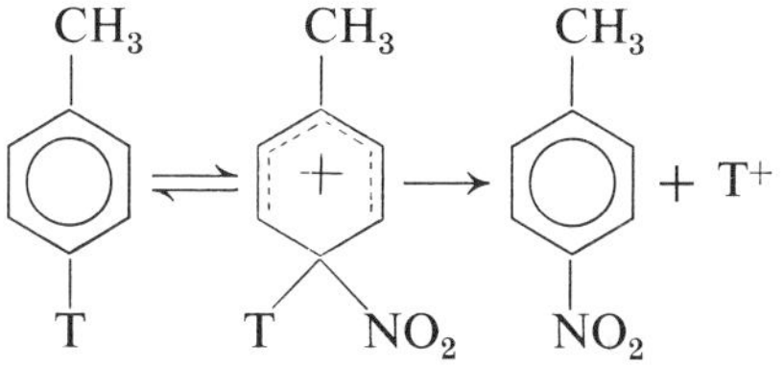

step is assumed to be rate-determining and the tritium carbon bond is broken in the second, nonrate-determining step.[15]   A more complex

[14] S. Winstein, T. G. Traylor, and G. S. Garner, *J. Am. Chem. Soc.* **77**, 3741 (1955); S. Winstein and T. G. Traylor, *J. Am. Chem. Soc.* **77**, 3747 (1955); S. Winstein and T. G. Traylor, *J. Am. Chem. Soc.* **78**, 2597 (1956); F. R. Jensen and L. H. Gale, *J. Am. Chem. Soc.* **81**, 1261 (1959)

[15] L. Melander, *Acta Chem. Scand.* **3**, 95 (1949)

mechanism with two intermediate charge transfer complexes (to be discussed later) seems to be more consistent with all the data on electrophilic aromatic substitution. The theory of electrophilic substitution reactions is well discussed by Bavin and Dewer[16] and Brown,[17] these reactions are important to the biochemist because many enzymic hydroxylations, both aliphatic and aromatic, are probably of this type.

CONCERTED REACTIONS

A concerted reaction is a reaction that occurs in one step. The definition of "one step" is not always clear but commonly it means that the carbonium ion, radical, or carbanion intermediate does not have time to give more than a single product. For example, if a carbonium ion gives a DL mixture of products from an optically active reactant, this is not a concerted reaction. Reactions which are catalyzed by an acid and a base at the same time are concerted reactions; an example is the enolization of ketones.

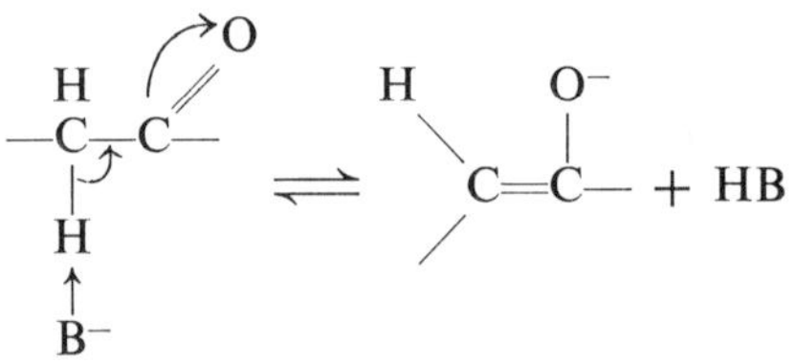

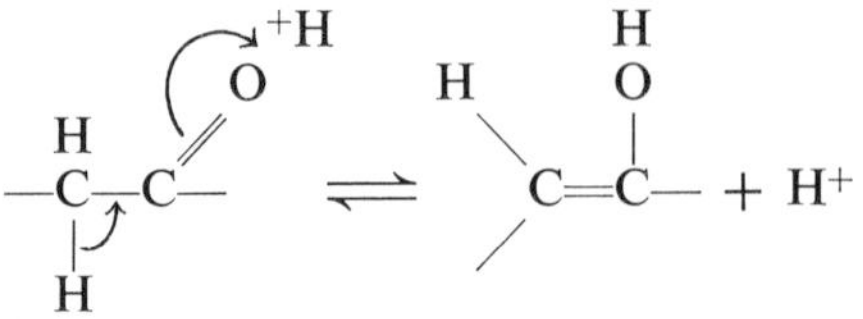

A very efficient mechanism is possible if the ketone is attacked by both an acid and a base. These reactions are certainly important in nonpolar

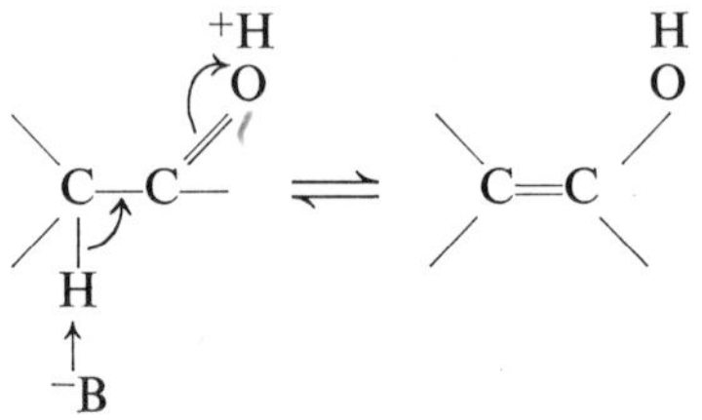

[16] P. M. G. Bavin and M. J. S. Dewar, *J. Chem. Soc.* **1956**, 164
[17] R. D. Brown, *J. Chem. Soc.* **1959**, 2224, 2232

solvents such as benzene and very probably important in aqueous solutions also. Swain has shown that the kinetics of mutarotation of glucose in aqueous solutions can be interpreted in terms of a concerted push-pull mechanism[18] where the base is designated as the nucleophile, N, and the acid as the electrophile, E. Swain points out that the great efficiency of

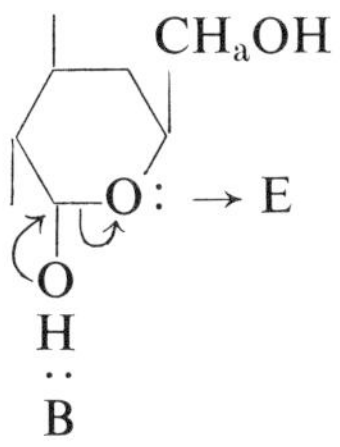

enzymes in catalyzing reactions may be the result of having both N and E on the same molecule in the proper position. Swain and Brown investigated catalysts with both N and E on the same molecule and found that 2-hydroxypyridine is an excellent catalyst for the mutarotation of tetramethyl glucose in benzene solution.[19] The kinetics are not third order with this catalyst but second order—first order in tetramethyl glucose and first order in 2-hydroxypyridine. The 2-hydroxypyridine must serve as both a nucleophilic reagent and an electrophilic reagent. This catalyst has both electrophilic and nucleophilic groups held in the correct positions on the same molecule (cf. section on entropy). A millimolar solution of

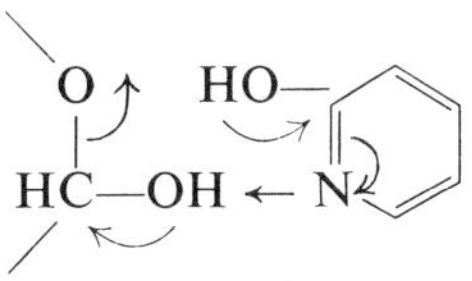

2-hydroxypyridine is 7000 times faster than millimolar phenol and millimolar pyridine. These results are obtained even though 2-hydroxypyridine is only 1/10,000th basic as pyridine and one hundredth as acidic as phenol.

Specific examples of concerted enzymic reactions are described by Koshland,[20] Boyer,[21] and Buchanan and Hartman.[22]

[18] C. G. Swain, *J. Am. Chem. Soc.* **72,** 4578 (1950)

[19] C. G. Swain and J. F. Brown, *J. Am. Chem. Soc.* **74,** 2538 (1952)

[20] D. E. Koshland, Jr., *Enzymes* Vol. I. Ed. by P. D. Boyer, H. Lardy, and K. Myrbach, Academic Press, (1959) p. 305

[21] P. D. Boyer, *Ann. Rev. Biochem.* **29,** 15 (1960)

[22] J. M. Buchanan and S. C. Hartman, *Advances in Enzymol.* **21,** 199 (1959)

METALS AS ACID CATALYSTS

Metals can catalyze[23] chemical reactions by (1) aiding in the gathering of reactants and thus increasing the entropy of activation; (2) stabilizing free radicals; and (3) acting as intermediates in reactions between one-electron and two-electron oxidants or reductants. A fourth and very important function of metals must be to act as general acid catalysts in reactions requiring a positive charge.[24] Protons are only available to the enzyme in high concentrations at low pH values, but metal ions carrying more than the one charge of hydrogen ion are available at physiological pH values. The effectiveness of a metallic ion as an acid catalyst increases with the charge on the ion, decreases with the radius of the ion, and depends upon the shielding effect of the d electrons.[25] The function of various metal ions as acid catalysts has been demonstrated in several model nonenzymic systems. Cupric and nickelic ions, for example, strongly catalyze the hydrolysis of the Schiff base shown below. The usual mechanism of

$$\text{S}\diagup\!\!-CH=N\diagup^{CH_2-CH_2}\diagdown N=CH-\diagdown_{\text{S}}$$

hydrolysis of a Schiff base would occur through attack by water on the carbon of the conjugate acid of the base. The positive charge on the nitrogen polarizes the $C=N$, making the carbon more positive and therefore more susceptible to nucleophilic attack by water.[26]

$$R-CH=N-R + H^+ \longrightarrow R-CH\overset{H_+}{=}\!\overset{}{N}-R$$
$$\underset{H_2O}{\nearrow}$$

The nickel or copper ion can perform the function of the hydrogen ion in the metal chelate of the Schiff base under less acidic conditions. The metal ion thus acts in this reaction as an acid catalyst. Decarboxylations

[23] R. J. P. Williams, *Special Lectures Biochem.*, University College London (1954) p. 100

[24] I. M. Klotz, *The Mechanism of Enzyme Action*, ed. by W. D. McElroy and B. Glass, Johns Hopkins Press (1954) p. 257

[25] L. E. Orgel, *Biochem. Soc. Symp. (Cambridge, Engl.)* **15**, 8 (1958)

[26] G. L. Eichorn and J. C. Bailar, Jr., *J. Am. Chem. Soc.* **75**, 2905 (1953); G. L. Eichorn and I. M. Trachtenberg, *J. Am. Chem. Soc.* **76**, 5183 (1954)

catalyzed by metal ions acting as acids will be discussed in the section on decarboxylation.

$$\begin{array}{c} CH_2 \!-\! CH_2 \\ \diagup \qquad \diagdown \end{array}$$

$$\text{S} \!-\! CH \!=\! N \cdots\!\! M^{2+}\!\! \cdots N \!=\! CH \!-\! \text{S}$$

$$H_2O$$

CHARGE TRANSFER COMPLEXES

Complexes between aromatic compounds and iodine, silver ion, or picric acid are familiar to all chemists. Mulliken and others[27] have pointed out that these molecular complexes may be formed between electron donor and electron acceptor molecules by the partial transfer of an electron from the donor to the acceptor. This may be described by the resonance forms I and II. In the ground state the complex is predominantly in form I but in the excited state it may be predominantly in form II.

$$\left[\begin{array}{cc} A\cdot \quad \cdot B & A^+ \quad :B^- \\ \text{I} & \text{II} \end{array} \right]$$

Typical charge transfer complexes are the benzene-iodine complex, the picrates, and perhaps some metal complexes. Charge transfer complex formation has been proposed to hold reduced diphosphoryridine nucleotide (DPNH) to substrates before actual reaction occurs.

Absorption spectra observed during the transition from the ground state, with the electron partially transferred from A to B, to the excited state, where there is a much greater transfer of the electron from A to B, are called charge transfer spectra. They have been described by Orgel[28] for metal complexes. Charge transfer spectra are quite intense: those of hemocyanin, laccase, and ascorbic acid oxidase show strong bands in the region around 600 mμ. These bands have extinction coefficients of 750–1200, whereas those of the cupric chelates are below 200. The intense bands may be the result of a transfer of an electron[29] from copper to an oxygen molecule or perhaps to protein. Riboflavin will form a complex with tryptophane and DPNH which has been described as a charge transfer type complex.[30]

[27] R. S. Mulliken, *J. Am. Chem. Soc.* **74**, 811 (1952); L. J. Andrews, *Chem. Rev.* **54**, 713 (1954); W. Brackman, *Rec. trav. chim.* **68**, 147 (1949)

[28] L. E. Orgel, *Quart. Rev.* **8**, 422 (1954)

[29] L. E. Orgel, *Biochem. Soc. Symp.* (*Cambridge, Engl.*) **15**, 8 (1958)

[30] I. Isenberg and A. Szent-Gyorgi, *Proc. Nat. Acad. Sci. U.S.* **44**, 857 (1958); I. Isenberg and A. Szent-Gyorgi, *Proc. Nat. Acad. Sci. U.S.* **45**, 1229 (1959)

"HIGH ENERGY" BONDS

Certain types of compounds, such as anhydrides, have a higher free energy of hydrolysis than normal esters. Although normal bonding occurs in these compounds, they are said to contain "high energy" bonds. The free energy of hydrolysis produces energy which is used elsewhere in the organism for mechanical motion or chemical synthesis.[31]

The most common compounds of this type are the anhydrides, of which an example is adenosine triphosphate. This compound hydrolyzes to adenosine diphosphate and phosphate ion at pH 7 and 30°C with a free energy[32] of −7.6 kcal, compared with a corresponding free energy of hydrolysis of a normal phosphate ester, glucose phosphate, of −3.2 kcal. Second row and lower elements are poor double-bond formers,[33] so that the phosphate-oxygen bond is strongly semipolar. This effect causes a large amount of electrostatic repulsion energy between the phosphates which is released on hydrolysis.[34] This probably accounts for much of the higher free energy of hydrolysis of a phosphate anhydride.

$$
\begin{array}{ccc}
O^- & & O^- \\
| & & | \\
-P^+ & -O- & P^+- \\
| & & | \\
O^- & & O^-
\end{array}
$$

Similarly "active sulfate," adenyl sulfate, has a high free energy of hydrolysis because of electrostatic effects. Adenyl acetate and acetyl phosphate are both anhydrides of a carboxylic acid and phosphoric acid.

$$
\begin{array}{ccc}
O^- & & O^- \\
| & & | \\
-P^+ & -O- & S^+=O \\
| & & | \\
O^- & & O^-
\end{array}
$$

Acetyl phosphate hydrolyzes with a free energy of −10.2 kcal at pH 7, compared with −7.2 kcal for ethyl acetate or −3.2 kcal for glucose-6-phosphate. A normal carboxylic acid ester has resonance forms as shown

[31] H. M. Kalckar, *Chem. Rev.* **28**, 71 (1941); F. Lipmann, *Advances in Enzymol.* **1**, 99 (1941)

[32] F. H. Carpenter, *J. Am. Chem. Soc.* **82**, 1111 (1960)

[33] K. S. Pitzer, *J. Am. Chem. Soc.* **70**, 2140 (1948)

[34] T. H. Hill and M. Morales, *J. Am. Chem. Soc.* **73**, 1656 (1951)

below. In anhydrides of phosphoric acids and carboxylic acids this type of resonance is hindered by the positive charge on the phosphorus atom.

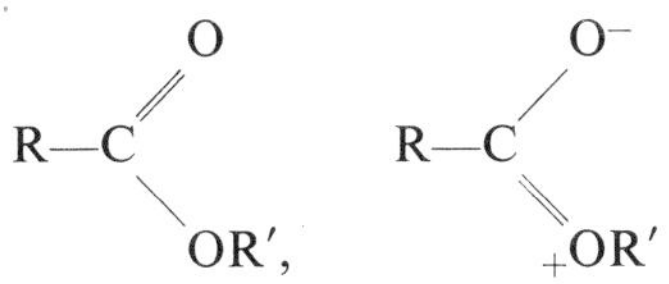

$$
R-C{\overset{\displaystyle O}{\diagdown}}_{OR'}, \qquad R-C{\overset{\displaystyle O^-}{\diagup}}_{+OR'}
$$

Less resonance makes the ester less stable, and the free energy of hydrolysis higher than that of a normal ester,

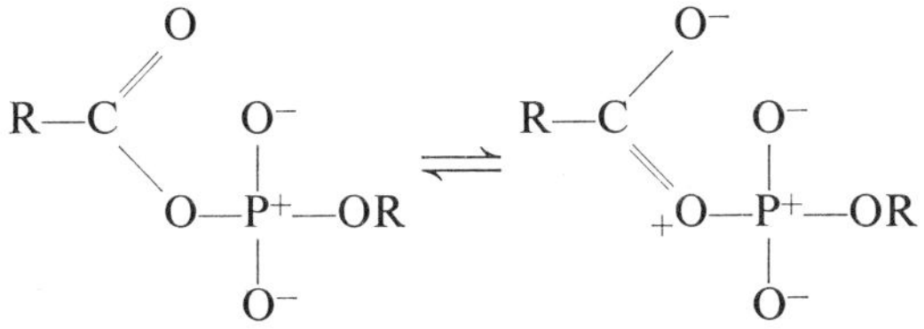

$$
R-C{\overset{O}{\diagdown}}_{O-\underset{\overset{|}{O^-}}{\overset{|}{P^+}}-OR} \quad O^- \rightleftharpoons \quad R-C{\overset{O^-}{\diagup}}_{+O-\underset{\overset{|}{O^-}}{\overset{|}{P^+}}-OR} \quad O^-
$$

Guanidinium phosphates such as creatine phosphate

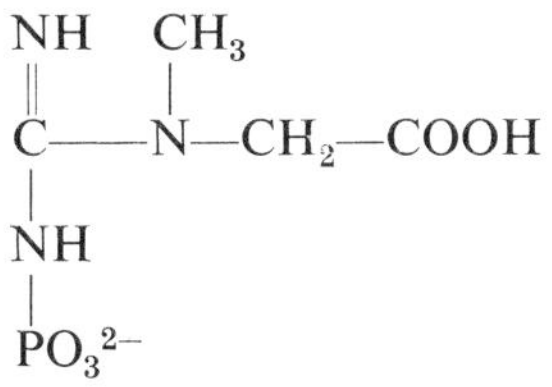

$$
\underset{\underset{\underset{PO_3{}^{2-}}{|}}{\overset{|}{NH}}}{\overset{\overset{NH}{\|}}{C}}\;\overset{\overset{CH_3}{|}}{-N}-CH_2-COOH
$$

and arginine phosphate

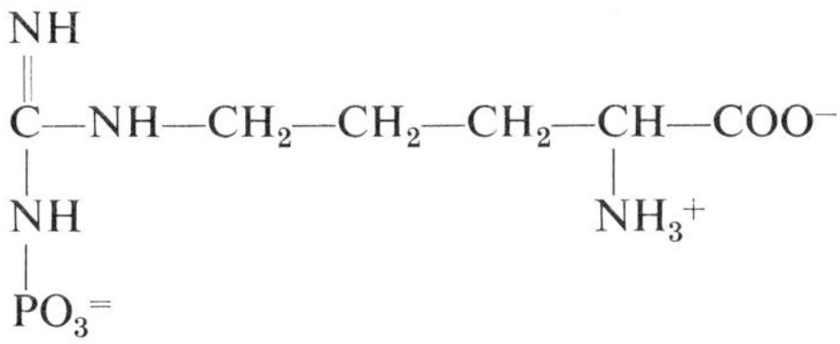

$$
\underset{\underset{\underset{PO_3{}^=}{|}}{\overset{|}{NH}}}{\overset{\overset{NH}{\|}}{C}}-NH-CH_2-CH_2-CH_2-\underset{\overset{|}{NH_3{}^+}}{CH}-COO^-
$$

also have a high free energy of hydrolysis. Creatine phosphate has a free energy of hydrolysis of -10.6 kcal at pH 7. The type of bonding changes when a phosphoric amide is hydrolyzed. An $N-P^+$ bond becomes an $O-P^+$ bond and an $O-H$ bond becomes an $N-H$ bond.[34]

$$N-P^+ + H_2O \longrightarrow N-H + HOP^+$$

The $O-P^+$ bond is more stable than an $N-P^+$ bond by 28 kcal, and an $O-H$ bond is more stable than an $N-H$ bond by 26.5 kcal, giving a resulting change in free energy of -1.5 kcal due to differences of bond energies.

Reactants		Products	
N—P$^+$		O—P$^+$	28
O—H	26.5	N—H	
	26.5		28

Difference −1.5 kcal.

This small difference in free energy can not account for the large free energy of hydrolysis of the guanidinium phosphates. The most important factor contributing to the large free energy of hydrolysis is the hindered guanidinium ion resonance in the phosphate ester.

Guanidines are strong bases because they combine with a proton to form guanidinium ions that are stabilized by several resonance forms.

$$\text{H}_2\text{N}\overset{\overset{\displaystyle \text{NH}}{\|}}{\text{—C—}}\text{NH}_2$$

$$\downarrow + \text{H}^+$$

$$\left[\ \text{NH}_2\overset{\overset{\displaystyle \text{NH}_2}{|}}{\text{—C}}\text{=N}^+\text{H}_2, \quad \text{NH}_2\overset{\overset{\displaystyle \overset{+}{\text{NH}_2}}{\|}}{\text{—C—}}\text{NH}_2, \quad \overset{+}{\text{NH}_2}\overset{\overset{\displaystyle \text{NH}_2}{|}}{\text{=C}}\text{—NH}_2\ \right]$$

One of these is less important in the guanidinium phosphates because of the adjacent phosphorus atom. However, all three forms are possible

$$\text{H}_2\text{N}\overset{\overset{\displaystyle \text{R}}{|}\,\overset{\displaystyle \text{NH}}{|}}{\text{—C}}\text{=}\overset{\overset{\displaystyle \text{H}}{|}}{\underset{+}{\text{N}}}\text{—}\overset{\overset{\displaystyle \text{O}^-}{|}}{\underset{\underset{\displaystyle \text{O}^-}{|}}{\text{P}^+}}\text{—OH}$$

after hydrolysis and this increase in resonance energy upon hydrolysis causes the free energy to be large.

Enol phosphates also have a large negative free energy of hydrolysis and in this reaction the free energy can be accounted for by the difference in bond energy between the enol and keto forms. The keto form of pyruvic acid is more stable than the enol form by 5.5 kcal. Addition of bond energies gives a difference of 18 kcal in favor of the keto forms.

Thiol esters also have a higher free energy of hydrolysis than normal oxygen esters. Biological examples are acetyl coenzyme A and acetyl lipoic acid. Acetyl coenzyme A has a free energy[35] of hydrolysis of −8.2 kcal at pH 7.

Thiol esters have less resonance than oxygen esters and this probably accounts for the larger free energy of hydrolysis. In normal esters,

[35] K. Burton, *Biochem. J.* **59**, 44 (1955)

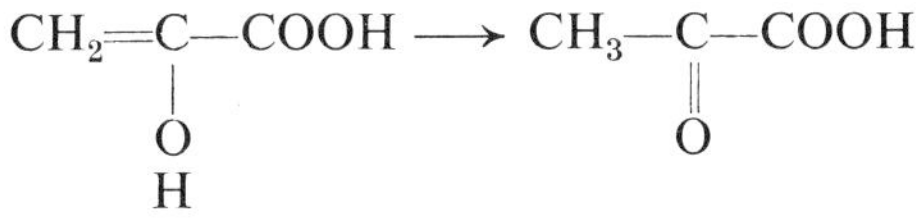

$$CH_2{=}C{-}COOH \longrightarrow CH_3{-}C{-}COOH$$

(left structure: CH₂=C—COOH with O—H substituent below the C)
(right structure: CH₃—C(=O)—COOH)

C—O	70		C—C	59
O—H	110		C—H	87
C=C	100		C=O	152
	280			298

resonance causes partial double bond formation between the carbon and the alcohol oxygen. Sulfur forms double bonds poorly[33] so that there will be less resonance stabilization in the thiol esters. This has two results;

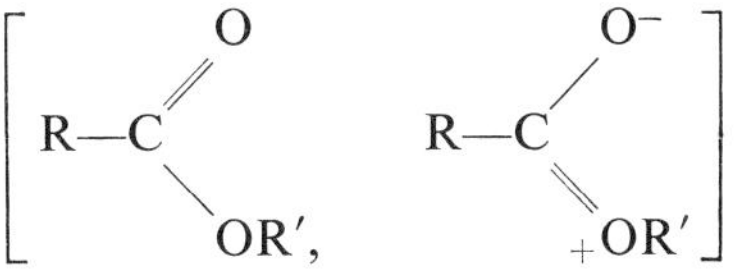

$$\left[\ R{-}C\overset{O}{\underset{OR'}{\diagdown\!\!\diagup}}, \qquad R{-}C\overset{O^-}{\underset{{}_+OR'}{\diagup\!\!\diagdown}}\ \right]$$

one is to make the free energy of hydrolysis higher and the other to make the carbonyl more like an aldehyde or ketone carboxyl and less like an ester carbonyl. In the later discussion it will be apparent that acetyl coenzyme A undergoes many reactions characteristic of an aldehyde.

An intermediate in the phospho-ketolase reaction (cf. section on Benzoin type reactions), 2-acetyl thiamine, probably has a high free energy of hydrolysis. Both strong repulsion between the positive nitrogen and the

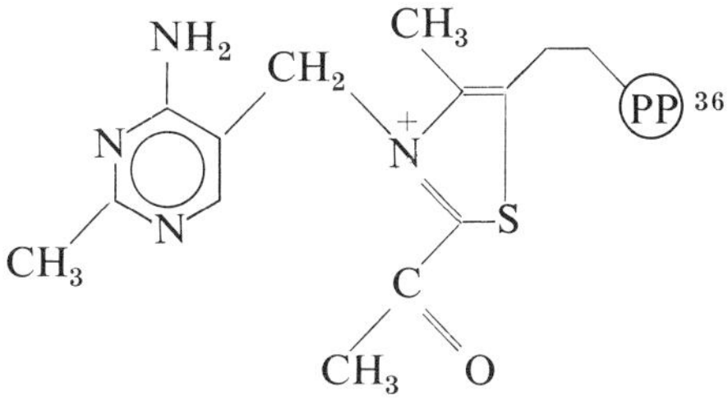

carbonyl dipole and the total lack of any ester type resonance would tend to make a high free energy of hydrolysis. The products of hydrolysis would be thiamine pyrophosphate and acetate ion.

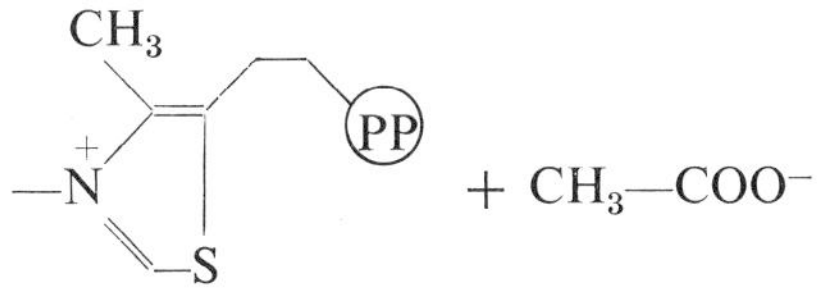

$+ CH_3{-}COO^-$

---

[36] PP will be used for the pyrophosphate group, and P for the phosphate group, throughout this book

part two

ESTERIFICATION AND HYDROLYSIS

Amides and esters

Mechanisms. When ethyl benzoate labeled with O^{18} in the carbonyl oxygen is hydrolyzed in either acid or basic solution to benzoic acid and ethanol, some of the O^{18} is lost to solvent.[1] These observations are consistent with the two following mechanisms for acid and for base catalyses.[1] The base-catalyzed ester hydrolysis proceeds by the attack of a hydroxide ion on the carbonyl of the ester followed by the decomposition of the intermediate to give the acid and alcoholate ion.

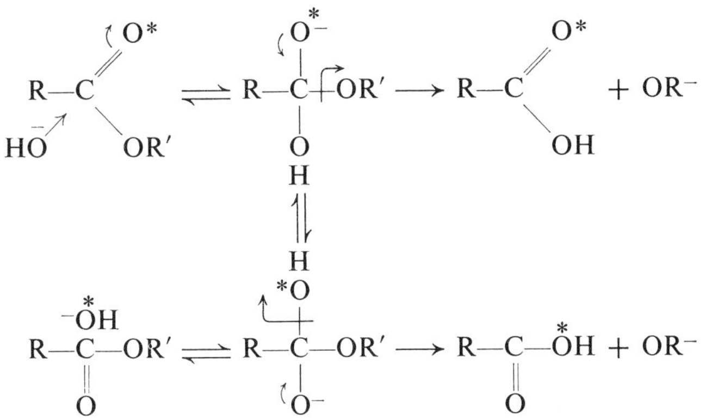

Acid-catalyzed ester hydrolyses proceed by the attack of water on the conjugate acid of the ester.

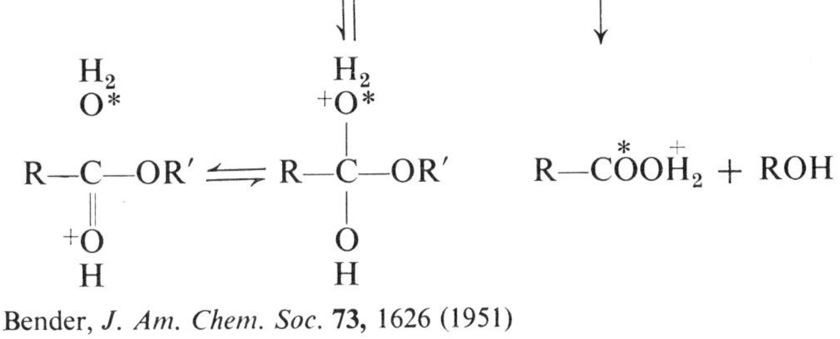

[1] M. L. Bender, *J. Am. Chem. Soc.* **73**, 1626 (1951)

A combination of these two mechanisms—attack by both an acid and a base—may be possible on an enzyme surface. If the enzyme were able to add a proton to the O-R group, the initial attack of the base on the carbon of the carbonyl group would be facilitated. Experimental evidence indicates that at least some esterases do have both acidic and basic groups.[2] The ability to present both acidic and basic groups simultaneously and at the proper positions to a substrate may be one of the most important functions of esterases.

An esterase may therefore catalyze a reaction by (1) allowing for a double displacement reaction; (2) holding the nucleophile (base) in the proper position for reaction; and (3) holding an acidic group in the proper position for reaction. The importance of these functions has been demonstrated by the study of models.

Models. Several model systems have shown that esters may be hydrolyzed by double displacement reactions. The hydrolysis of 2-4-dinitrophenyl benzoate when catalyzed by O^{18} labeled acetate ion produces O^{18} labeled benzoate ion. This result is consistent with a double displacement reaction proceeding through an anhydride.[3] The acetate ion attacks to form a mixed anhydride of acetic and benzoic acid. Water may attack this anhydride on either the carbonyl group of the benzoyl group or the acetyl group. Attack on the acetyl group would give labeled benzoate ion.

Several models of esterases have demonstrated that the reaction is much faster if the nucleophile is held in the right position for reaction. The hydrolysis of salicyl acetate is independent of pH in the range 4.5 to 9.5 where the carboxyl group is ionized. The carboxyl group must act as a nucleophile displacing the acetate ion to form the acetic salicylic anhydride which subsequently hydrolyzes to salicylic acid and acetic acid.[4] The

---

[2] I. B. Wilson and F. Bergmann, *J. Biol. Chem.* **186**, 683 (1950)
[3] M. L. Bender and M. C. Neveu, *J. Am. Chem. Soc.* **80**, 5388 (1958)
[4] E. R. Garrett, *J. Am. Chem. Soc.* **79**, 3401 (1957)

hydrolysis of ethyl acid phthalate[5] is similarly independent of pH in the range 5 to 7. The carboxylate group must again act as the nucleophile. The fact that these rates are independent of the pH shows that there is no catalysis by H^+ or OH^- as there is in the usual hydrolysis of an ester.

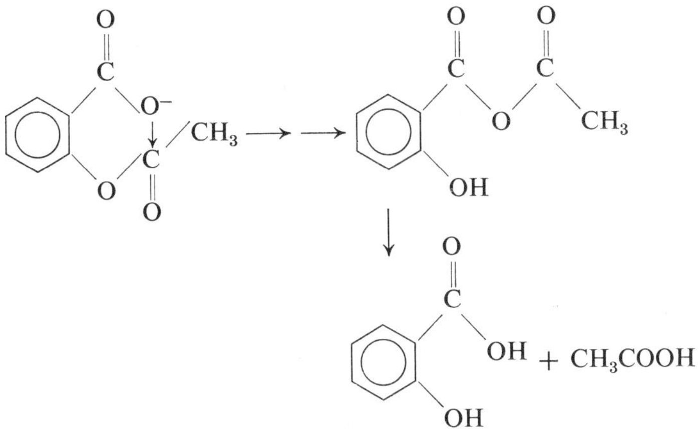

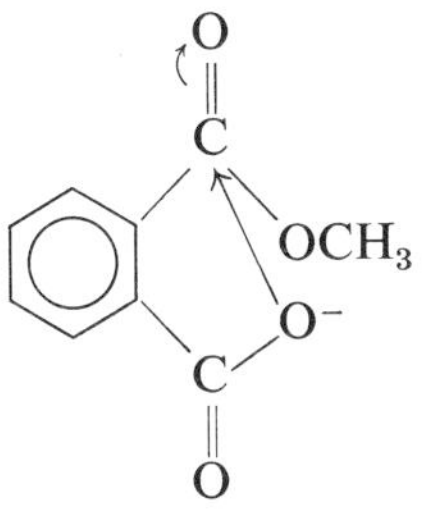

Similar demonstrations of the importance of holding the nucleophile in the correct position are found in the work of Morawetz and co-workers[6] who found that a polymer of 9 mole per cent *p*-nitrophenyl methacylate and 91 mole per cent acrylic acid will hydrolyze approximately 10^6 times as fast as *p*-nitrophenyl pivalate in the pH range 5 to 6. The latter compound exhibits the normal acid or basic catalysis, but hydrolysis of the polymer is independent of pH in the range 6 to 10 where the carboxyl groups are ionized. This implies that the attacking group is the carboxylate ion. The reaction is rapid because the carboxylate ion is in the correct position to attack.

[5] M. L. Bender, F. Chloupek, and M. C. Neveu, *J. Am. Chem. Soc.* **80**, 5384 (1958)

[6] P. E. Zimmering, E. W. Westhead, Jr., and H. Morawetz, *Biochim. et Biophys. Acta* **25**, 376 (1957)

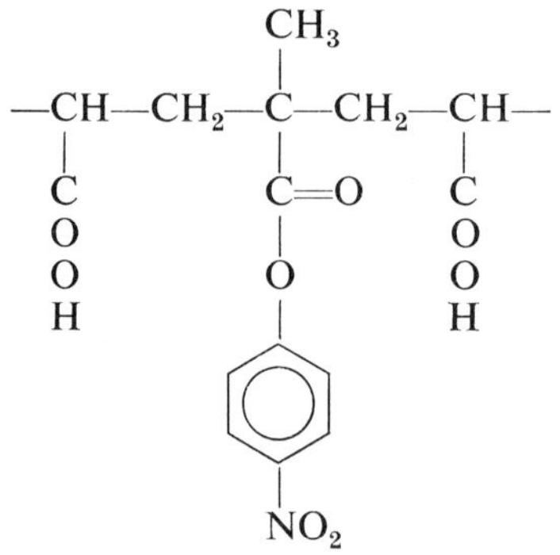

Polymer

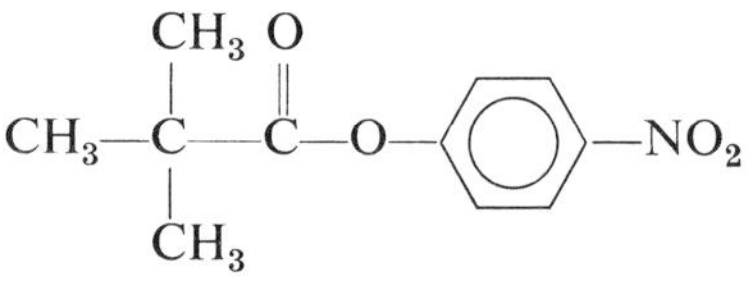

p-Nitrophenyl pivalate

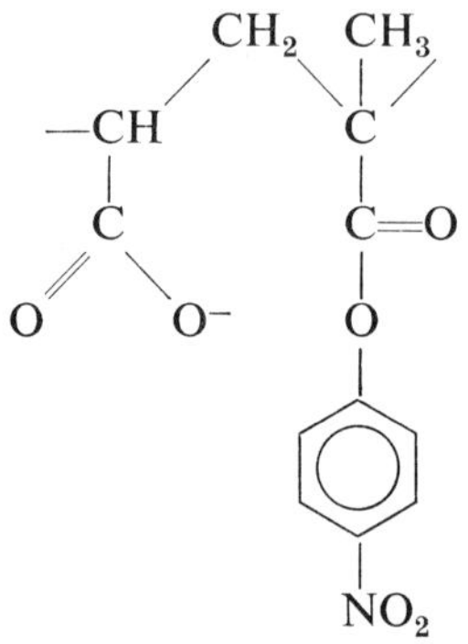

Other esterase models have demonstrated the importance of holding the acidic group in the correct position. Bender[7] has found that phthalamic acid is hydrolyzed 10^5 times as fast as benzamide at pH 3. The rate is independent of the pH in the range 1.3 to 2.6 but decreases at higher pH

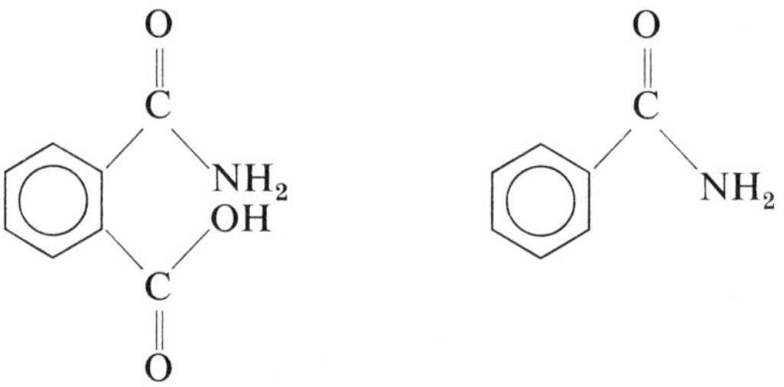

values. The undissociated phthalamic acid is therefore the reactive species and hydrogen ion is not involved in the mechanism. When phthalamic acid labeled with C^{13} in the amide group was hydrolyzed in H_2O^{18} and the phthalic acid was decarboxylated, the CO_2 was found to contain both

[7] M. L. Bender, *J. Am. Chem. Soc.* **79**, 1258 (1957)

$C^{13}O^{16}O^{18}$ and $C^{12}O^{16}O^{18}$. These results[8] with O^{18} in the CO_2 from both the amide and the carboxyl group indicate that at one stage in the reaction these groups must have been equivalent. These data were interpreted as the simultaneous attack by the carboxyl group and protonation of the amide nitrogen to form the symmetrical anhydride.

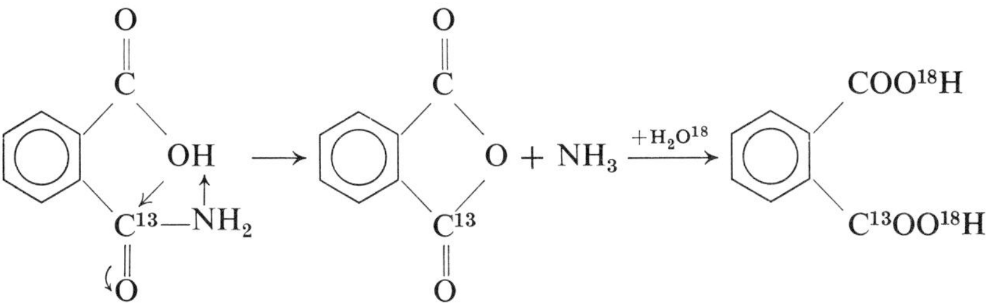

Certain esterase models have been made which combine nucleophilic and acidic groups on the same molecule. The imidization of an acrylic acid copolymer containing 3 mole per cent *p*-nitroacrylanilide proceeds at a maximum rate at pH 5 and decreases in rate at lower and higher pH values. The pH dependence thus obeys the common bell-shaped curve typical of so many enzymic reactions. These results have been interpreted in a mechanism requiring both an ionized and an unionized carboxyl group for the reaction. At lower pH values both groups are unionized and at higher pH values both are ionized.

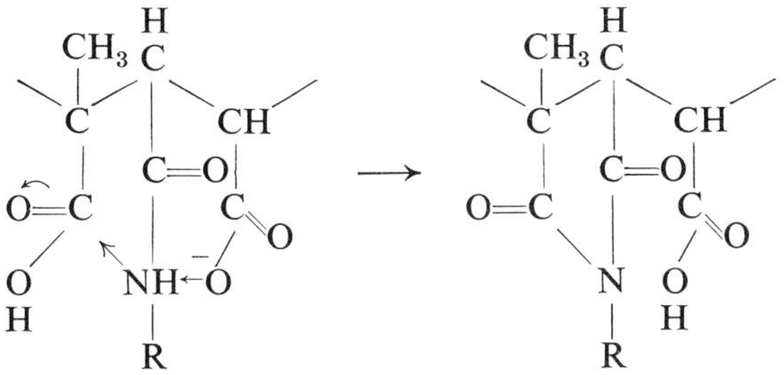

The hydrolysis of the half salicyl ester of succinic acid[9] also demonstrates the advantage of both an acidic and a basic group held in the proper position on the same molecule. This ester, I, hydrolyzes much faster at pH 4 and has a pH dependence entirely different from that of the related esters, II and III.

[8] M. L. Bender, Y.-L. Chow, and F. Chloupek, *J. Am. Chem. Soc.* **80,** 5380 (1958)
[9] H. Morawetz and I. Oreskes, *J. Am. Chem. Soc.* **80,** 2591 (1958)

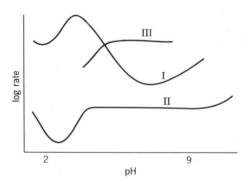

The rate of hydrolysis is greatest at pH 4 and decreases at either lower or higher pH values, again giving a bell-shaped pH dependence. The maximum concentration of the ionic species with the aromatic carboxyl group ionized and the aliphatic carboxyl group unionized would occur at

pH 4, the peak of the bell-shaped curve. The high rate of reaction and the dependence of the rate on pH is therefore consistent with a mechanism in which the aromatic carboxyl group serves as a nucleophile and the aliphatic carboxyl group as an electrophile.

Histidine catalysis. Studies[10] of the pH dependence of the rates of chymotrypsin-catalyzed reactions and of the photo-oxidation of chymotrypsin are in agreement with the hypothesis that a histidine in the enzyme takes part in the catalysis. The imidazol portion of the histidine presumably functions as the catalyst because imidazole has been shown to be a good

[10] H. Gutfreund and J. M. Sturtevant, *Biochem. J.* **63**, 656 (1956); L. Weil and A. R. Buchert, *Federation Proc.* **11**, 307 (1952)

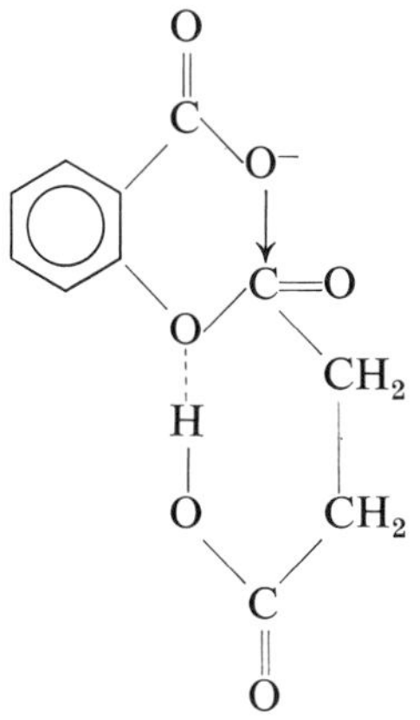

catalyst for the hydrolysis of phenyl acetates[11] in a double displacement reaction. The imidazole displaces the phenylate ion which in turn is displaced by water.

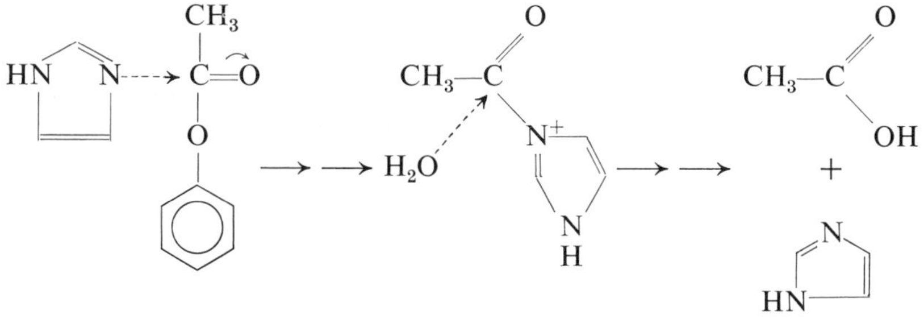

The ester, I, is hydrolyzed at a rate almost identical to that of the chymotrypsin *p*-nitrophenyl acetate complex.[12] Two factors account for the fast hydrolysis: (1) the imidazole is in the correct position to attack the carbonyl group, and (2) the imidazole is an excellent nucleophile.[13]

Metal catalysis. The enzyme carboxypeptidase contains zinc,[14] which presumably plays some role in its proteinase activity. Interestingly, the hydrolysis of amino acid esters and amides is catalyzed by metal ions; for example, copper, cobalt, and manganese all catalyze the hydrolysis of amino acid esters. The metal ion can act as a proton does, by polarizing

[11] M. L. Bender and B. W. Turnquest, *J. Am. Chem. Soc.* **79**, 1652, 1656 (1957); T. C. Bruice and G. L. Schmir, *J. Am. Chem. Soc.* **79**, 1663 (1957)

[12] T. C. Bruice and J. M. Sturtevant, *Biochim. et Biophys. Acta* **30**, 208 (1958); T. C. Bruice and J. M. Sturtevant, *J. Am. Chem. Soc.* **81**, 2860 (1959)

[13] T. C. Bruice and R. Lapinski, *J. Am. Chem. Soc.* **80**, 2265 (1958)

[14] J. E. Coleman and B. L. Vallee, *J. Biol. Chem.* **235**, 390 (1960)

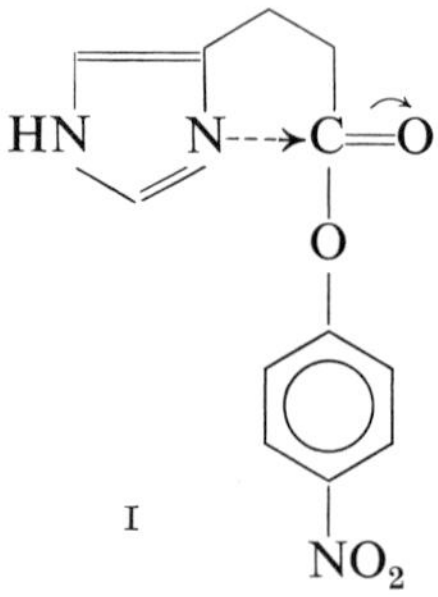

$$\text{HN} \quad \text{N---} \rightarrow \text{C} \overset{\frown}{=} \text{O}$$

$$\text{I} \qquad \text{NO}_2$$

the carbonyl group and thus aiding attack by water. The hydrolysis of glycine amide is catalyzed by cupric ion.[15]

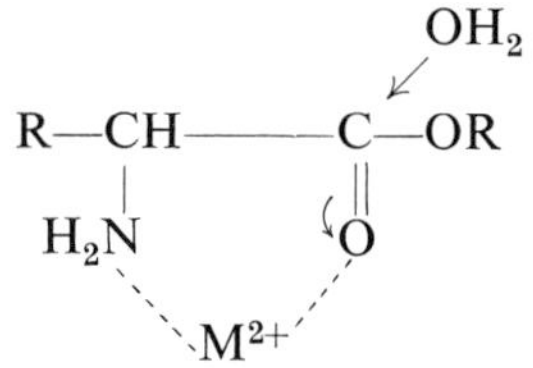

$$\text{R---CH--------C---OR}$$
$$\text{H}_2\text{N} \qquad \text{O}$$
$$\text{M}^{2+}$$

Thiol group catalysis. The proteinases ficin and papain both have thiol groups essential for enzyme activity.[16] Thiol groups have been found to catalyze hydrolytic reactions in model reactions.

A thiol group is a very good nucleophile and could serve as a catalyst in a double displacement reaction. For example, orthomercaptobenzoic acid is a good catalyst for the hydrolysis of *p*-nitrophenyl acetate.[17] The

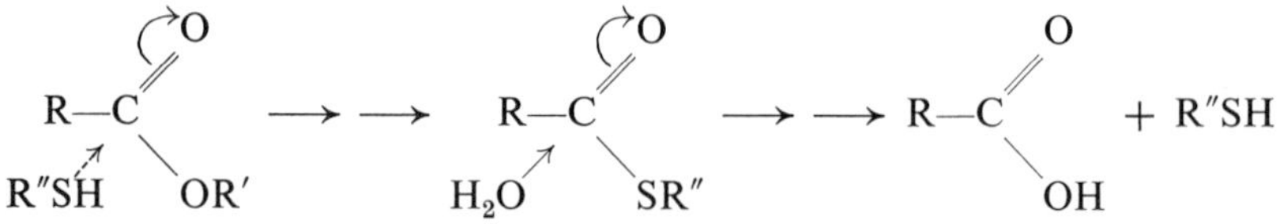

$$\text{R---C} \xrightarrow{} \xrightarrow{} \text{R---C} \xrightarrow{} \xrightarrow{} \text{R---C} + \text{R}''\text{SH}$$

catalytically active species has been found by pH studies to be the dianion. In a proposed mechanism the thiophenolate ion attacks the paranitrophenylacetate to form a thiol ester. The orthocarboxylate ion then attacks the thiol ester to form a mixed benzoic-acetate anhydride and this is hydrolyzed with water to give the products. The rate-determining step was found to be the hydrolysis of the thiol ester.

[15] L. Meriweather and F. H. Westheimer, *J. Am. Chem. Soc.* **78,** 5119 (1956); B. R. Rabin, *Biochem. Soc. Symp.* (*Cambridge, Engl.*) **15,** 21 (1958)
[16] E. L. Smith, *J. Biol. Chem.* **233,** 1392 (1958)
[17] G. R. Schonbaum and M. L. Bender, *J. Am. Chem. Soc.* **82,** 1900 (1960)

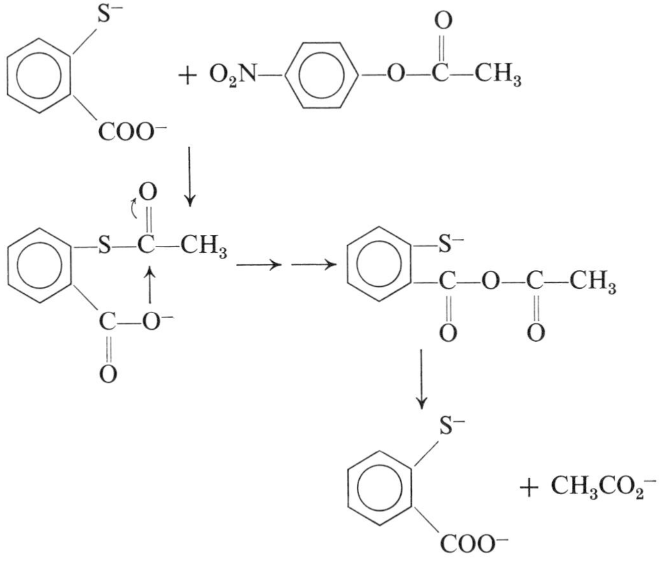

A carboxylate ion is required for this step so that the pK dependence of the overall reaction rate shows an inflection at approximately pH 4. Interestingly, papain and ficin also show inflections in their rate versus pH curves at approximately pH 4. Various mechanisms utilizing the nucleophilic properties of sulfur have been suggested to account for the enzyme activity.[18]

Unknown active centers. Very fine mechanistic studies have been made of several enzymes for which the exact nature of the active center is still unknown. These enzymes include lipase, aryl sulfatase, and acetyl cholinesterase. They are only grouped together here because of lack of knowledge which will enable us to classify them elsewhere.

Lipase catalyzes the hydrolyses of lipids and certain other esters. The lipase-catalyzed hydrolyses of phenyl acetates show much less dependence upon the electronic structure of phenyl acetate than the previously discussed nonenzymic imidazole catalysis. Hammett's reaction constant, ρ,[19] which measures the dependence of a reaction on electron density, is 0.12 for the lipase-catalyzed reaction compared with 1.95 for the imidazole-catalyzed reaction.[20] The smaller dependence of the lipase-catalyzed

---

[18] E. L. Smith, *J. Biol. Chem.* **233**, 1392 (1958)

[19] L. P. Hammett, *Physical Organic Chemistry*, McGraw-Hill Book Co., Inc., New York (1940) p. 184

[20] T. C. Bruice and G. L. Schmir, *J. Am. Chem. Soc.* **79**, 1663 (1957); T. C. Bruice and G. L. Schmir, *J. Am. Chem. Soc.* **80**, 148 (1958)

reaction on the ester structure means the enzyme must have a method of stabilizing charges so efficient that the stabilization of charges by substituents becomes less important.

Stabilization of charges is probably a function of all enzymes. A low dependence of rate on substituents may therefore be a general characteristic of enzyme catalyzed reactions.

The hydrolysis of aryl sulfates catalyzed by aryl sulfatase has been shown to proceed faster with substituents such as nitro groups on the benzene ring which withdraw electrons from the ring.[21] Groups such as a *p*-amino group which donate electrons to the ring hinder the reaction. These facts are in agreement with a mechanism in which water attacks the sulfur displacing a phenolate ion. If this mechanism obtains, the oxygen of the ester should remain on the benzene ring. Experiments with O^{18} have shown this to be true.[22]

$$\langle\bigcirc\rangle - O + S - OH$$

The kinetics of hydrolysis of acetyl choline by acetyl cholinesterase have been shown by Wilson and co-workers[23] to be consistent with a double displacement reaction in which each displacement follows the normal ester hydrolysis mechanism. The first attack on the carbonyl was assumed to be by the enzyme and the acyl enzyme hydrolyzes by a normal hydrolysis. This type of a mechanism, which requires that the alcoholic oxygen leave

$$R - C \overset{O}{\underset{OR'}{\big\langle}} \longrightarrow R - C + OR \longrightarrow R - C \overset{O}{\big\langle} + \bar{O}R$$
$$\text{Enz.} \qquad\qquad \text{Enz.} \qquad\qquad \text{Enz.}$$

with the alcoholate ion, has been tested by studying the hydrolysis of thiolacetic acid. Acetylcholinesterase will hydrolyze thiolacetic acid to acetic acid and hydrogen sulfide,[24] thereby exchanging oxygen for sulfur in agreement with the normal ester hydrolysis mechanism shown above. The pH dependence of the enzyme-catalyzed reaction may be interpreted in terms of a basic and acidic group at the reactive center.[25] The enzyme is presumably then both an acidic and basic catalyst in which the acidic group

[21] K. S. Dodgson, B. Spencer, and K. Williams, *Biochem. J.* **64**, 216 (1956)

[22] B. Spencer, *Biochem. J.* **69**, 155 (1958)

[23] I. B. Wilson, F. Bergmann, and D. Nachmanson, *J. Biol. Chem.* **186**, 781 (1950)

[24] E. B. Wilson, *Biochim. et Biophys. Acta* **7**, 520 (1951)

[25] I. B. Wilson and F. Bergmann, *J. Biol. Chem.* **186**, 683 (1950)

places a proton on the carbonyl oxygen of the ester and the basic group attacks the carbon of the carbonyl. The pK of these groups corresponds to a phenolic group and an imidazole group. The mechanism may be first esterification of the phenol and subsequent hydrolysis catalyzed by the imidazole.

Inhibition studies and substrate specificities studies all agree with the theory that the positive nitrogen of the acetyl choline is bound to a negative charge on the enzyme. Model studies have demonstrated how well such a charge interaction can speed the rate of reaction. A study of the kinetics of the catalyzed hydrolysis of *o*-nitrophenyl hydrogen oxalate anion has given the following results:

	pK	$k_2 \times 10^2$
Aniline	4.58	95
Pyridine	5.23	248
4-aminopyridine	9.17	1,460,000
4-aminopyridinium ion	−6.3	1–3
2-aminopyridine	7.14	61
2-aminopyridinium ion	−7.6	2.1

Two points are of interest in these data. The cation, 2-aminopyridinium ion, is about as good a catalyst as 4-aminopyridinium ion, although the 4-aminopyridinium ion is ten times more basic. More surprising, 2-amino-pyridinium ion is 1/30 as good a catalyst as 2-aminopyridine but $1/10^{14.7}$ as basic as 2-aminopyridine. Evidently, 2-aminopyridinium ion is a much better catalyst than would be expected from its basicity. This has been explained by an electrostatic attraction between substrate and catalyst. Electrostatic attraction between enzyme and substrate must be an important factor in the enzymic hydrolysis of charged substrates such as acetyl choline by cholinesterase.

Phosphates

Hydrolysis. The large number of negative charges on the oxygens around the phosphorus is an important factor in phosphate ester hydrolysis. These charges hinder the attack by a nucleophilic reagent such as hydroxide ion.[26]   Metals, for example, magnesium and manganese, will commonly neutralize these charges and catalyze the reaction.   Orthophosphate ion will attack adenosine triphosphate if the charges are neutralized by manganous ion[27] to form adenosine diphosphate and pyrophosphate.

An anion formed close to or held close to the phosphorus may have a very great advantage over anions in solution that have to overcome the negative shell around the phosphorus.   Salicyl phosphate, which has a carboxyl ion held close to the phosphorus, is hydrolyzed quite rapidly.[28] The attacking group is the carboxylate ion and the reaction proceeds through a double displacement.   Similar reactions occur in the catechol-catalyzed hydrolysis of fluorophosphate esters.[29]

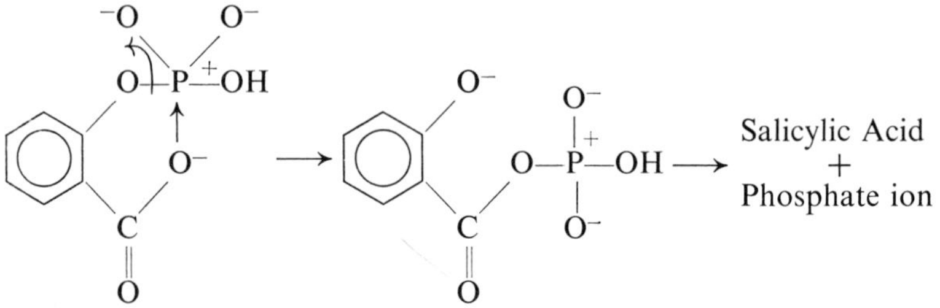

Esterification by a coupled oxidation.   Coenzyme Q_{10}, with the structure shown below where $n = 10$, has been isolated from beef heart mitochondria.[30]   Similar quinones in this series, with $n = 6, 7, 8,$ and 9, have

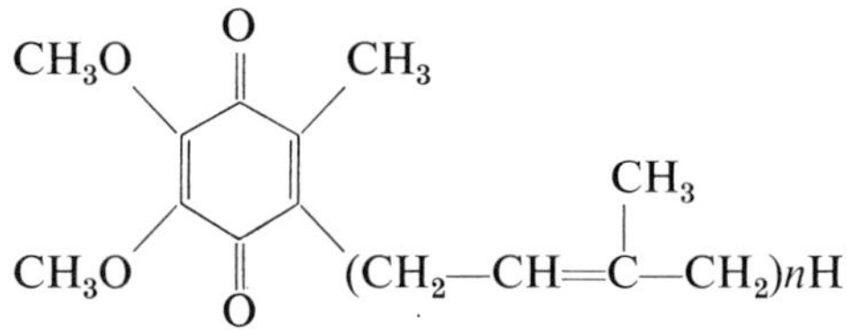

been isolated from microbial sources.   These quinones are widespread in nature and the suggestion has been made that they perform a role in

[26] For a review of phosphate chemistry, see A. Todd, *Proc. Nat. Acad. Sci. U.S.* **45**, 1389 (1959)

[27] J. M. Lowenstein, *Biochim. et Biophys. Acta* **28**, 206 (1958)

[28] J. D. Chanley, E. M. Gindler, and M. Sobotka, *J. Am. Chem. Soc.* **74**, 4347 (1952); J. D. Chanley and E. Feageson, *J. Am. Chem. Soc.* **77**, 4002 (1955)

[29] J. Epstein, D. H. Robenblat, and M. M. Demek, *J. Am. Chem. Soc.* **78**, 341 (1956)

[30] D. E. Wolf, C. H. Hoffman, N. R. Trenner, B. H. Arison, C. H. Shunk, B. O. Linn, J. F. McPherson, and K. Folkers, *J. Am. Chem. Soc.* **80**, 4751 (1958); L. Lester, F. L. Crane, and Y. Hatefi, *J. Am. Chem. Soc.* **80**, 4752 (1958)

oxidative phosphorylation.[31]   There is no definite proof that quinones are necessary in this reaction; however, it is possible to write mechanisms of action to suggest how they may function.

Reduction, the addition of two electrons to the quinone, will form a dianion which will normally add two protons to form a hydroquinone. In the presence of phosphate ion, the anion could attack the phosphorus atom, thus displacing a hydroxyl group to form an ester.

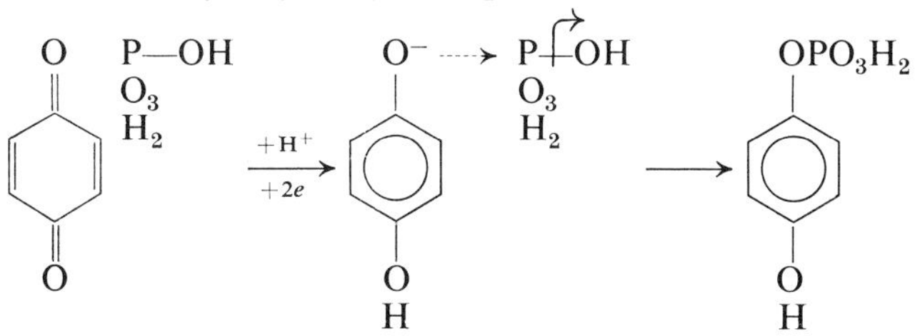

Hydroquinone is a weak acid, and the second dissociation of hydroquinone would be quite small, so that the dianion would be an extremely reactive species at physiological pH values.   In terms of "high energy" this ion contains much of the "reduction energy."   This reaction is comparable to the

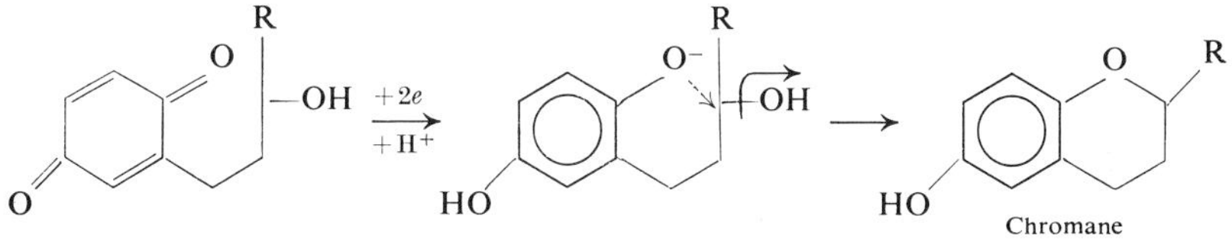

formation of chromanes on the reduction of quinones. Normally a phenoxide ion would not be able to penetrate the negative shell of charge around the phosphate ion to cause reaction. However, this ion is formed by reduction after the relatively neutral oxygen has already penetrated the negative shell. Subsequent oxidation of the hydroquinone phosphate will produce

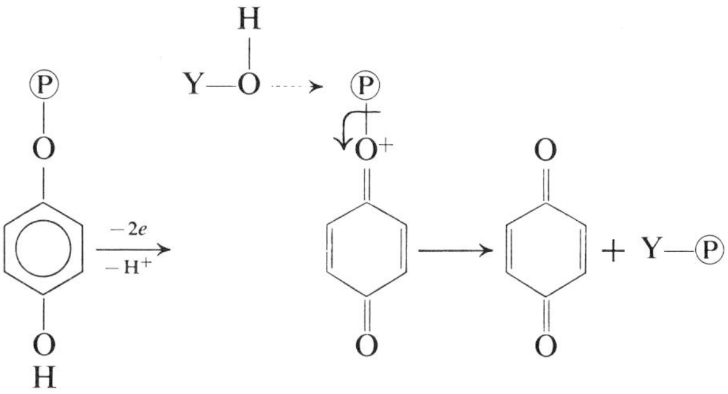

[31] R. L. Lester and F. L. Crane, *J. Biol. Chem.* **234**, 2169 (1959); Y. Hatefi, R. L. Lester, and T. Ramasarma, *Federation Proc.* **17**, 238 (1958)

a very active phosphorylating species.[32] Attack on the phosphorus by a nucleophilic reagent, Y, would displace the easily displaceable quinone and effect a phosphorylation of the Y. The quinone is easily displaceable because the positive oxygen is in an excellent position to leave with a pair of electrons. A model reaction is the iodine oxidation of naphthohydroquinone phosphate in ethanol which produces ethyl phosphate.[33] A

similar mechanism of phosphorylation by means of oxidation of hydroquinone phosphates has been proposed by Harrison.[34]

ELIMINATION REACTIONS

Nonoxidative

Mechanisms. The elimination of H-X from $\overset{\diagdown}{\underset{\diagup}{CH}}-\overset{\diagup}{\underset{\diagdown}{CX}}$ to form an olefin can occur by three different general mechanisms. (1) The anion X^- may be lost first to give an intermediate carbonium ion which can subsequently lose a proton to form an olefin. (2) The proton may be lost first to form an intermediate carbanion which can lose the anion X^- in a subsequent reaction to form the olefin. (3) Both proton and X^- anion may be lost in a single concerted step to form the olefin. In the carbonium ion mechanism or the carbanion mechanism either step may be rate determining so that a total of five different mechanisms are possible. Alberty and co-workers[35] have pointed out how it is possible to distinguish between at least four of these mechanisms by means of deuterium tracers. Two measurements can be made. The rate of exchange of $\overset{\diagdown}{\underset{\diagup}{CH}}-\overset{\diagup}{\underset{\diagdown}{CX}}$ with D_2O can be compared with the rate of the overall reaction to olefin. If

[32] V. M. Clark, G. W. Kirby, and A. Todd, *Nature* **181,** 1650 (1958)
[33] T. Wieland and F. Patterman, *Angew. Chem.* **70,** 313 (1958)
[34] K. Harrison, *Nature* **181,** 1131 (1958)
[35] R. A. Alberty, W. G. Miller, and H. F. Fisher, *J. Am. Chem. Soc.* **79,** 3973 (1957)

exchange is faster than olefin formation, this indicates that an intermediate anion is formed. The other measurement is the deuterium rate effect, i.e., does $\diagdown\text{CD}\!\!-\!\!\text{CX}\diagup$ eliminate DX more slowly than or at the same rate as $\diagdown\text{CH}\!\!-\!\!\text{CX}\diagup$ eliminates HX. A deuterium rate effect occurs when the C—H bond is broken in the slow rate-determining step. The correlation of the results of these experiments with the mechanisms is shown in the table below:

I Carbonium ion

$$\diagdown\text{CH}\!\!-\!\!\text{CX}\diagup \rightleftharpoons \diagdown\text{CH}\!\!-\!\!\overset{+}{\text{C}}\diagup + X^- \rightleftharpoons \diagdown\text{C}\!\!=\!\!\text{C}\diagup + H^+$$

		D-rate	D-exchange	X-rate
A	Slow	Fast	No	No	Yes
B	Fast	Slow	Yes	No	No

II Carbanion

$$\diagdown\text{CH}\!\!-\!\!\text{CX}\diagup \rightleftharpoons \diagdown\text{C}^-\!\!-\!\!\text{CX}\diagup + H^+ \rightleftharpoons \diagdown\text{C}\!\!=\!\!\text{C}\diagup + X^-$$

			D-rate	D-exchange	X-rate
A	Slow	Fast	Yes	No	No
B	Fast	Slow	No	Yes	Yes

III Concerted

$$\diagdown\text{CH}\!\!-\!\!\text{CX}\diagup \rightleftharpoons \diagdown\text{C}\!\!=\!\!\text{C}\diagup + H^+ + X^-$$

D-rate	D-exchange	X-rate
Yes	No	Yes

Mechanism *IA* is found in nonenzymic reactions. The rate of elimination only depends upon the concentration of RX so that the reaction rate is first order in RX and is commonly called E_1. Mechanisms 1*B* and II*A* have not been found in any reaction. Slow ionizations of hydrogen ions are difficult to imagine. Mechanism II*B* is commonly thought of as an addition reaction in nonenzymic chemistry. It commonly occurs with olefins that are activated by a group such as a carbonyl group and is called a Michael Reaction. Mechanism III, the concerted elimination reaction, occurs in many nonenzymic reactions. It requires a base to pull off the proton, so that the reaction is second order, first order in base and first order in RX, and is commonly abbreviated by the symbol E_2. These mechanisms will now be discussed in detail.

Carbonium ion mechanisms. If the X leaves first a carbonium ion will be formed. The carbonium ion is planar and rotation of the single bond between the carbon atoms allows the most stable olefin isomer or mixture of isomers to be formed. An example of this reaction is the acid-catalyzed

$$\diagdown \!\!CH\!\!-\!\!CX\diagup \rightleftharpoons \diagdown \!\!CH\!\!-\!\!\overset{+}{C}\diagup \rightleftharpoons \diagdown \!\!C\!\!=\!\!C\diagup + H^+$$

formation of an olefin from some alcohols. First the conjugate acid of the alcohol is formed.

$$ROH + H_3O^+ \rightleftharpoons RO^+H_2 + H_2O$$

and this species loses water to form a carbonium ion.

$$\diagdown \!\!CH\!\!-\!\!C\!\!-\!\!O^+H_2 \rightleftharpoons \diagdown \!\!CH\!\!-\!\!\overset{+}{C}\diagup + H_2O$$

The elimination of water from malic acid to form fumaric acid is catalyzed by the enzyme fumarase.[36] This reaction has been thoroughly studied both kinetically and mechanistically[37] by Alberty, Massey, and co-workers. The kinetic will be discussed only as the results apply to the mechanism. The elimination catalyzed by the enzyme was found to be trans by a study of the addition reaction in deuterium oxide. The stereo position of the deuterium in the deuterated malic acid relative to the hydroxyl group was determined by nuclear magnetic resonance.[38] The hydrogen-carbon bond does not break in the rate-determining step because deutero-1-malate loses HOD at the same rate as the nondeuterated compound loses H_2O.[39] The rate-determining step must therefore be cleavage of the C—O bond. A prior fast removal of hydrogen ion has been shown not to occur because malate ion and fumarase do not incorporate deuterium into the malate ion faster than can be accounted for by the back reaction from fumaric acid.[40]

[36] E. M. Scott and R. Powell, *J. Am. Chem. Soc.* **70**, 1104 (1948)
[37] V. Massey, *Biochem. J.* **53**, 67 (1953); R. M. Bock and R. A. Alberty, *J. Am. Chem. Soc.* **75**, 1921 (1953); R. A. Alberty, V. Massey, C. Frieden, and A. R. Fuhlbrigge, *J. Am. Chem. Soc.* **76**, 2485 (1954); C. Frieden, R. C. Wolfe, and R. A. Alberty, *J. Am. Chem. Soc.* **79**, 1523 (1957); R. A. Alberty and W. H. Peirce, *J. Am. Chem. Soc.* **79**, 1526 (1957); R. A. Alberty and B. M. Koerber, *J. Am. Chem. Soc.* **79**, 6379 (1957); R. A. Alberty and G. G. Hammes, *J. Phys. Chem.* **62**, 154 (1958)
[38] O. Gawron and T. P. Fondy, *J. Am. Chem. Soc.* **81**, 6333 (1959)
[39] H. F. Fisher, C. F. Frieden, J. S. M. McKee, and R. A. Alberty, *J. Am. Chem. Soc.* **77**, 4436 (1955); R. A. Alberty, W. G. Miller and H. F. Fisher, *J. Am. Chem. Soc.* **79**, 3973 (1957)
[40] R. A. Alberty, W. G. Miller, and H. F. Fisher, *J. Am. Chem. Soc.* **79**, 3973 (1957)

These observations are consistent with a rate-determining formation of a carbonium ion followed by a rapid ionization of water. Retention of configuration, although a planar carbonium ion is formed, has been explained by the enzyme holding the carbonium ion tight enough to prevent rotation.

$$\begin{matrix} \diagdown \diagup \\ \text{C--}\overset{+}{\text{O}}\text{H}_2 \\ | \\ \text{CH} \\ \diagup \diagdown \end{matrix} \rightleftharpoons \begin{matrix} \diagdown \diagup \\ \text{Enz---C}^+ \\ | \\ \text{CH} \\ \diagup \diagdown \end{matrix} \rightleftharpoons \begin{matrix} \diagdown \diagup \\ \text{C} \\ \| \\ \text{C} \\ \diagup \diagdown \end{matrix}$$

This mechanism indicates that the enzyme has two functional groups, an acidic group to add a proton to the hydroxyl and a basic group to pull the proton off carbon. The pK's of these groups were determined by a thorough study of the pH dependence of the fumarase reaction. The pK's were found[41] to be 6.2 and 6.8 on the free enzyme, 5.3 and 7.3 in the enzyme-fumarate complex, and 6.6 and 8.4 in the enzyme-malate complex. These groups are possibly a carboxyl group and an imidazole group.[41]

A similar mechanism occurs in the aconitase reaction. The aconitase-catalyzed labeling of citric acid in D_2O occurs at the same rate as the formation of aconitic acid.[42] This result is in agreement with a carbonium ion mechanism similar to the fumarase reaction. This reaction has also been shown to be a *trans* elimination.[43]

Carbanions. Carbanion mechanisms commonly occur when the carbanion is stabilized by conjugation with a carbonyl group of an aldehyde, ketone, ester, or acid. Addition reaction, the reverse of the elimination reaction, with this type of conjugated anions are called Michael reactions.

$$\left[\begin{matrix} & & \text{O} \\ & & \diagup\!\!\!\diagup \\ \text{--}\overset{-}{\text{C}}\text{H--C} \\ & & \diagdown \end{matrix} \quad , \quad \begin{matrix} & & \text{O}^- \\ & & \diagup \\ \text{--CH}\!=\!\text{C} \\ & & \diagdown \end{matrix} \right]$$

The addition of ammonia to mesaconic acid, catalyzed by the enzyme β-methylaspartase, has been shown to proceed through an anion because the enzyme catalyzes a fast deuterium exchange[44] between water and the product, β-methylaspartic acid. The reaction must, therefore, be a Michael reaction in which ammonia is added to a conjugated acid. The reaction

---

[41] V. Massey and R. A. Alberty, *Biochim. et Biophys. Acta* **13**, 354 (1954); C. Frieden and R. A. Alberty, *J. Biol. Chem.* **212**, 859 (1955)

[42] S. Englard and S. P. Colowick, *J. Biol. Chem.* **226**, 1047 (1957)

[43] O. Gawron, A. J. Glaid, A. La Monte, and S. Gary, *J. Am. Chem. Soc.* **80**, 5856 (1958)

[44] H. J. Bright, R. E. Lundin, and L. L. Ingraham: Unpublished research

occurs at pH 8 so that the intermediate must have two negative charges on one carboxyl group.

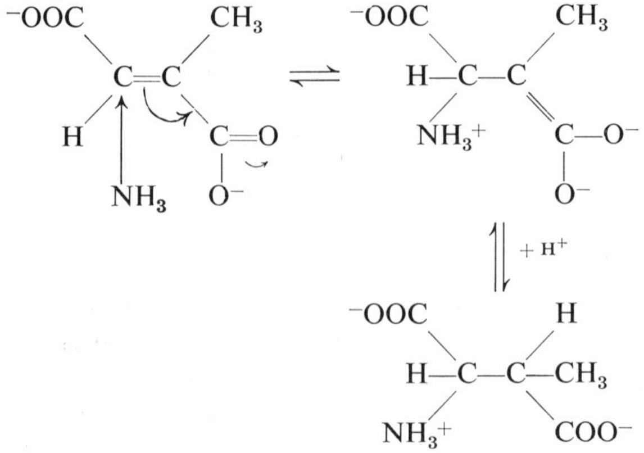

$$
\begin{array}{ccc}
\text{structure} & \rightleftharpoons & \text{structure}
\end{array}
$$

A dianion such as this would normally be quite hard to form, but the enzyme requires both K^+ ion and Mg^{2+} ion. These metal ions presumably help to stabilize the dianion. A nuclear magnetic resonance study of the product of the reaction, β-methylaspartic acid has shown that the elimination is trans.

Stern and del Campillo[45] have found that crotonase will isomerize crotonic acid to isocrotonic acid and that crotonase contains essential sulfhydryl groups. They have postulated an addition of the enzyme to the crotonic acid, presumably via a Michael type mechanism, followed by a displacement of the enzyme by water.

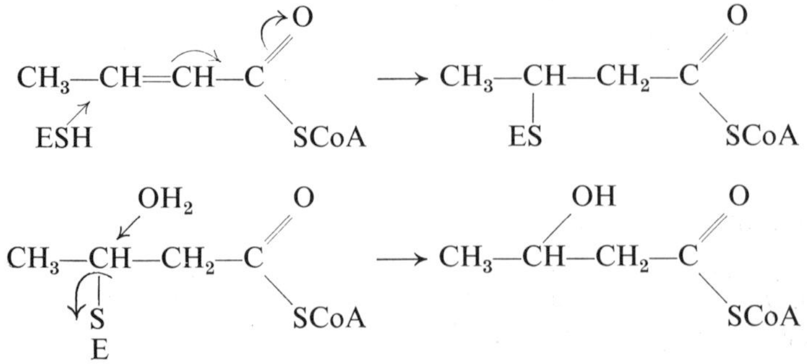

Catalyzed by pyridoxal. The coenzyme pyridoxal phosphate, catalyzes, among other reactions of amino acids, both α-β and β-γ elimination reactions. Essentially, these are carbanion reactions in which the proton is lost before the negative group. Examples of the α-β elimination are the

[45] J. R. Stern and A. del Campillo, *J. Biol. Chem.* **218**, 985 (1956)

reaction of serine or cysteine to give pyruvic and water or hydrogen sulfide.[46]

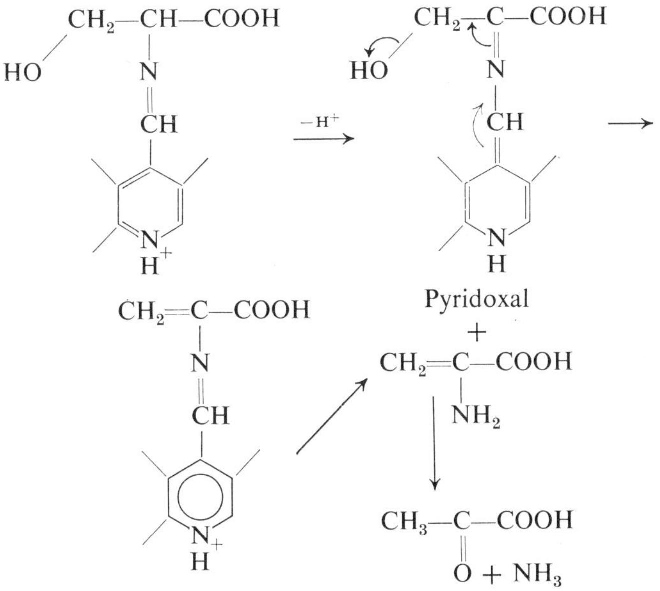

CH₂—CH—COOH with HO, N, CH ... reaction scheme

Pyridoxal phosphate stabilizes the carbanion formed on the loss of H^+ by placing the electron pair on the nitrogen of the pyridoxal.

Pyridoxal phosphate will also catalyze β-γ eliminations. A mechanism has been written for the conversion of phosphohomoserine to threonine. Isotopic studies using deuterium and heavy oxygen support the mechanism on page 54.[47]

Pyridoxal will also catalyze the reaction of homoserine to α-ketobutyric acid. The mechanism must be similar to the previous reaction, except that

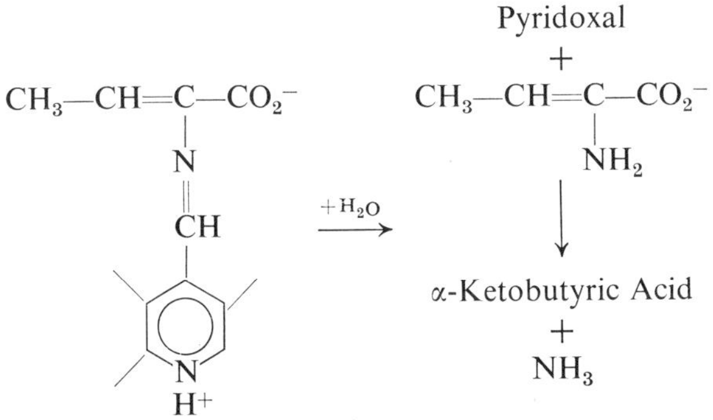

[46] D. E. Metzler and E. E. Snell, *J. Biol. Chem.* **198**, 353 (1952)
[47] M. Flavin and C. Slaughter, *J. Biol. Chem.* **235**, 1112 (1960)

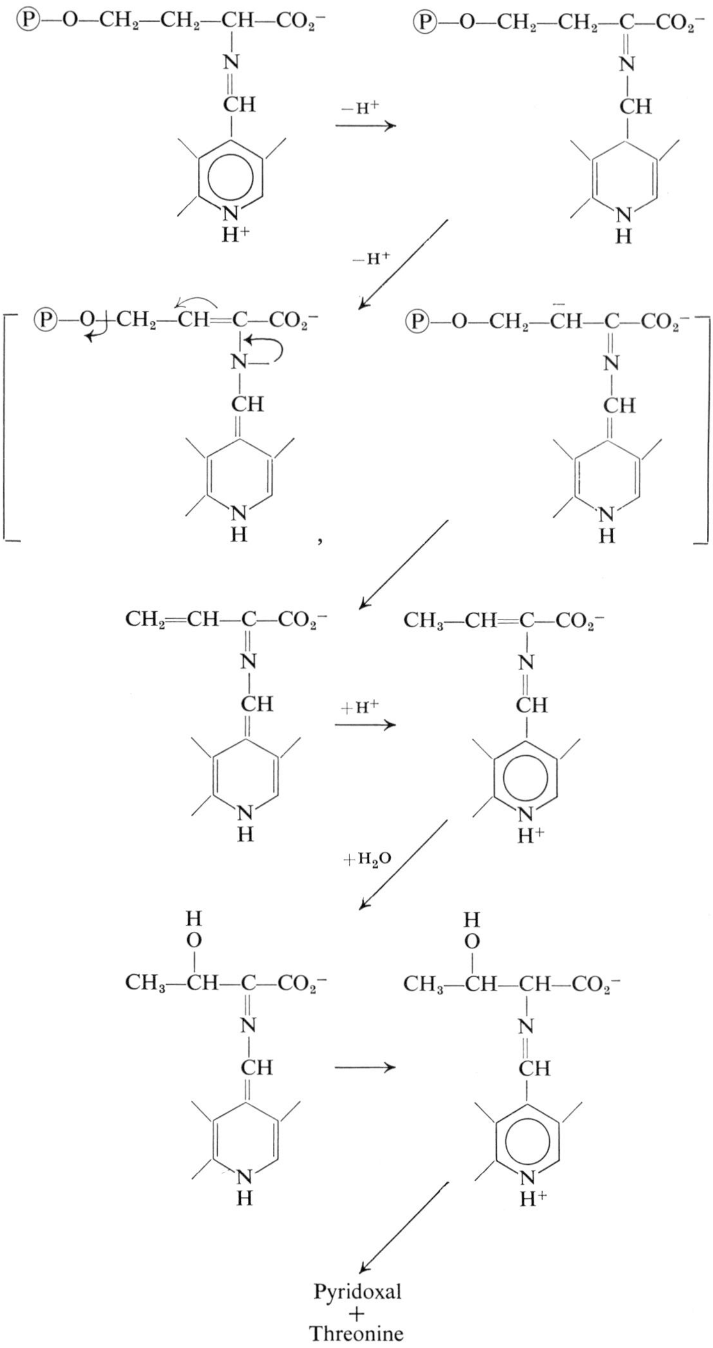

$$\text{(P)}-O-CH_2-CH_2-CH-CO_2^-$$

$$\xrightarrow{-H^+}$$

$$\text{(P)}-O-CH_2-CH_2-C-CO_2^-$$

$$-H^+$$

$$\left[\ \text{(P)}-O\,|\,CH_2-CH=C-CO_2^- \quad , \quad \text{(P)}-O-CH_2-\overset{-}{CH}-C-CO_2^- \ \right]$$

$$CH_2=CH-C-CO_2^- \qquad CH_3-CH=C-CO_2^-$$

$$\xrightarrow{+H^+}$$

$$+H_2O$$

$$CH_3-\underset{H}{\overset{O}{CH}}-C-CO_2^- \qquad CH_3-\underset{H}{\overset{O}{CH}}-CH-CO_2^-$$

$$\longrightarrow$$

Pyridoxal
+
Threonine

the olefin does not add water but now is hydrolyzed directly to give a vinyl amine, which in turn gives α-ketobutyric acid.

A similar reaction catalyzed by the enzyme cystathionase, which also contains pyridoxal, is the cleavage of cystathione to cysteine and α-keto-butyric acid.[48]

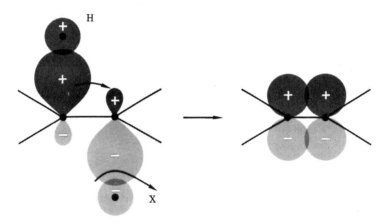

The mechanism of this reaction must be the same as that for homoserine except cysteine is eliminated instead of water.

Concerted eliminations. Concerted eliminations are always *trans,* i.e., the H^+ and Y^- are eliminated from opposite sides of the bond. This is because the electrons of the hydrogen-carbon bond displace the leaving group in a reaction comparable with a nucleophilic displacement reaction. As the electrons from the C—H bond attack the rear of the carbon holding the Y group, the small lobe on the rear of the sp^3 orbital gradually increases

in size (rehybridizes) to form the lobe of a p orbital. The hydrogen ion must be eliminated *trans* to the leaving group X, which must form a fairly stable entity upon leaving. An example of this type of reaction is the Hoffman degradation of quaternary ammonium salts catalyzed by hydroxide ion.[49] At present there are no known enzymic elimination reactions that are concerted.

[48] Y. Matsuo and D. M. Greenberg, *J. Biol. Chem.* **234**, 516 (1959)
[49] V. J. Shiner, Jr. and M. L. Smith, *J. Am. Chem. Soc.* **80**, 4095 (1958)

Oxidative elimination reactions

Conjugated. The enzyme acyl dehydrogenase catalyzes the oxidation of butyryl coenzyme A to crotyl coenzyme A by flavin adenine dinucleotide. Flavins can form semiquinone intermediates in oxidation (cf. discussion of flavin oxidations) so that this reaction is probably a radical reaction. The reaction between two radicals to form an olefin is well known.[50] Radicals

$$\text{R}\cdot + \overset{\diagdown}{\underset{\diagup}{\text{C}}}\text{H}\!-\!\overset{\diagup}{\text{C}}\cdot \longrightarrow \text{RH} + \overset{\diagdown}{\underset{\diagup}{\text{C}}}\!=\!\overset{\diagup}{\underset{\diagdown}{\text{C}}}$$

in turn may be formed by the oxidation of an anion as in the base-catalyzed oxidation of 2-nitropropane.[51]

$$\underset{\underset{\text{CH}_3}{|}}{\overset{\overset{\text{CH}_3}{|}}{\text{HC}}}\!-\!\text{NO}_2 + \overline{\text{O}}\text{H} \longrightarrow \underset{\underset{\text{CH}_3}{|}}{\overset{\overset{\text{CH}_3}{|}}{-\text{C}}}\!-\!\text{NO}_2 + \text{H}_2\text{O}$$

$$\underset{\underset{\text{CH}_3}{|}}{\overset{\overset{\text{CH}_3}{|}}{^-\text{C}}}\!-\!\text{NO}_2 + \text{R}\cdot \longrightarrow \underset{\underset{\text{CH}_3}{|}}{\overset{\overset{\text{CH}_3}{|}}{\cdot\text{C}}}\!-\!\text{NO}_2 + \text{R}^-$$

Oxidation (loss of electrons) is more easily understandable with a negatively charged ion than with a neutral molecule. With these facts in mind, a plausible mechanism may be written for the eliminations catalyzed by acyl dehydrogenase. The coenzyme A ester allows the formation of an anion (cf. discussion of adol condensations) which the flavin of the enzyme will oxidize to a radical. Subsequent reaction with the flavin radical

$$\text{R}\!-\!\text{CH}_2\!-\!\text{CH}_2\!-\!\overset{\diagup\text{O}}{\underset{\diagdown\text{SCoA}}{\text{C}}} \longrightarrow \text{R}\!-\!\text{CH}_2\!-\!\overline{\text{C}}\text{H}\!-\!\overset{\diagup\text{O}}{\underset{\diagdown\text{SCoA}}{\text{C}}}$$

(semiquinone) will form the desired olefin. The dienol[52] of succinic acid

$$\text{R}\cdot + \text{R}\!-\!\text{CH}_2\!-\!\overset{\cdot}{\text{C}}\text{H}\!-\!\overset{\diagup\text{O}}{\underset{\diagdown\text{SCoA}}{\text{C}}} \longrightarrow \text{RH} + \text{R}\!-\!\text{CH}\!=\!\text{CH}\!-\!\overset{\diagup\text{O}}{\underset{\diagdown\text{SCoA}}{\text{C}}}$$

[50] A. F. Bickel and W. A. Waters, *Rec. trav. chim.* **69**, 312 (1950)
[51] A. G. Russell, *J. Am. Chem. Soc.* **76**, 1595 (1954)
[52] This idea was originally expressed by R. H. Abeles in a private conversation

will form the comparable radical in the succinic dehydrogenase reaction. A free radical has been detected in the succinic dehydrogenase reaction.[53]

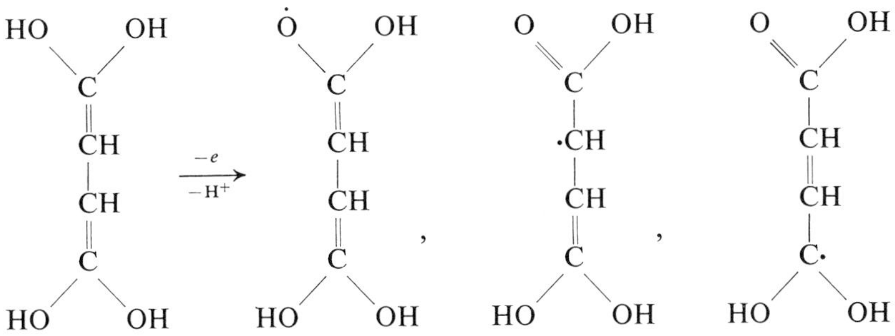

$$
\begin{array}{cccc}
\underset{HO}{}\overset{OH}{\diagdown}\underset{}{C} & \underset{HO}{}\overset{OH}{\diagdown}\underset{}{C} & \underset{HO}{}\overset{OH}{\diagdown}\underset{}{C} & \underset{HO}{}\overset{OH}{\diagdown}\underset{}{C}
\end{array}
$$

Homoconjugated. Some extremely interesting elimination reactions occur in the metabolism of fatty acids. These are the oxidations of unsaturated fatty acids to form 1,4 olefins which are not conjugated. Linoleic acid is oxidized to γ-linolenic acid and finally to arachidonic acid.[54]

$$CH_3—(CH_2)_4—(CH{=}CH—CH_2)_2—(CH_2)_6—COOH$$
linoleic

$$CH_3—(CH_2)_4—(CH{=}CH—CH_2)_3—(CH_2)_3—COOH$$
γ-linolereic

$$CH_3—(CH_2)_4—(CH{=}CH—CH_2)_4—(CH_2)_2—COOH$$
Arachidonic

The formation of allyl radial or carbonium ion may be understood because these are stabilized by resonance. However, these intermediates would

$$[—\overset{\cdot}{C}H{=}CH—CH—, \quad —CH—CH{=}\overset{\cdot}{C}H—]$$
$$[—\overset{+}{C}H{=}CH—CH—, \quad —\overset{+}{C}H—CH{=}CH—]$$

lead to 1,3 diolefins. In order to form a 1,4 diolefin it is necessary to form a homoallyl radical or carbonium ion.

$$—\overset{+}{C}H—CH_2—CH{=}CH—$$
$$—\overset{\cdot}{C}H—CH_2—CH{=}CH—$$

Carbonium ions of the type shown above are known only in very rigid systems such as cholesterol. In these systems the p orbitals are held in position so that resonance stabilization may occur through partial bonding between the 2 and 4 carbon atoms.

This type of ion does not occur in aliphatic systems where rotation may take place between the 2 and 3 carbons and between the 3 and

[53] H. Beinert and R. H. Sands, *Biochem. Biophys. Res. Commun.* **3**, 41 (1960)
[54] J. F. Mead and D. R. Howton, *J. Biol. Chem.* **229**, 575 (1957)

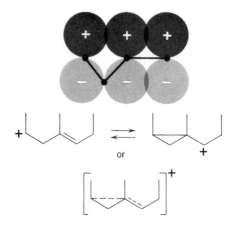

4 carbons. Homoallyl ions may be possible on an enzyme surface where the fatty acid is held fairly rigidly. The analogous homoallyl radicals have been looked for[55] but no evidence for their existence has been found.

DECARBOXYLATION

Mechanisms

When an acid is decarboxylated the carbon dioxide leaves without a pair of electrons. If the decarboxylation is to proceed at a practical rate, the pair of electrons left on the R· group must be stabilized by some means. In a β-keto acid[56] this is accomplished by placing the electrons on the

$$R—CO_2^- \longrightarrow R^- + CO_2$$

carbonyl oxygen. The proton on the acid probably aids the process, making the oxygen a better electron sink.

$$R—\overset{\overset{\displaystyle O}{\|}}{C}\overset{\frown}{CH_2}\overset{\frown}{CO_2^-} \longrightarrow R—\overset{\overset{\displaystyle}{\underset{-O}{|}}}{C}=CH_2 + CO_2$$

$$R—C\overset{CH_2}{\underset{\overset{O}{\|}}{\diagup}}\overset{\diagdown}{C=O} \longrightarrow R—C\overset{CH_2}{\underset{\overset{O}{|}}{\diagup}} + CO_2$$

[55] S. J. Cristol and R. P. Arganbright, *J. Am. Chem. Soc.* **79**, 6039 (1957); S. J. Cristol, G. D. Brindell, and J. A. Reeder, *J. Am. Chem. Soc.* **80**, 635 (1958)
[56] F. H. Westheimer and W. A. Jones, *J. Am. Chem. Soc.* **63**, 3283 (1941)

Catalysis by metals

Divalent metal ions strongly catalyze the decarboxylation of α,α-dimethyloxalacetic acid. The metal ions act as an electron sink for the electron pair and the first product is the metal chelate of the enol. The enol was observed as the first product by spectroscopy and bromine titration. The enzymic decarboxylation of oxalacetic acid also requires

divalent metal ions.[57] However, there are differences between the Mn^{2+}-catalyzed and the enzyme-catalyzed decarboxylation of oxalacetic acid.[58] The metal-catalyzed decarboxylation is about 6 per cent slower if the carboxyl group contains C^{13}, whereas the enzymic decarboxylation is the same for the C^{13} carboxyl labeled compound as for the C^{12}. The manganese-catalyzed reaction is the same in D_2O as in H_2O but the enzymic reaction is considerably slower in D_2O. Evidently the C—C cleavage is rate determining for the manganese-catalyzed reaction but not for the enzyme-catalyzed reaction. Possibly the ketonization of the enol is rate determining for the enzyme-catalyzed reaction. The C—C bond breaks in the enzyme-catalyzed reaction more than 10^8 times as fast as in the Mn^{2+} catalyzed reaction.

The carboxylation reactions to form β-keto acids proceed by a reverse mechanism. The enol form is carboxylated to give the keto acid.[59] That the enzymic carboxylation of phosphoenol pyruvate first produces the keto form and not the enol was shown by carboxylating in deuterium oxide and showing that the keto acid contained no deuterium.[60] An enol would have gained deuterium upon rearrangement to the keto acid.

Electrophilic displacements

The acid-catalyzed decarboxylation of aromatic acids proceeds by the electrophilic attack of a proton displacing the $COOH^+$ group.[61] Possibly some enzymic decarboxylations, for example, the formation of indole

[57] R. Steinberger and F. H. Westheimer, *J. Am. Chem. Soc.* **73**, 429 (1951); J. F. Speck, *J. Biol. Chem.* **178**, 315 (1949)
[58] S. Seltzer, G. A. Hamilton, and F. H. Westheimer, *J. Am. Chem. Soc.* **81**, 4018 (1959)
[59] M. Calvin, *Federation Proc.* **13**, 697 (1954)
[60] T. T. Tchen, F. A. Loewus, and B. Vennesland, *J. Biol. Chem.* **213**, 547 (1955)
[61] W. M. Schubert, J. Donohue, and J. D. Gardner, *J. Am. Chem. Soc.* **76**, 9 (1954)

rings and the oxidation of fatty acids catalyzed by fatty acid peroxidase, are electrophilic displacement reactions.

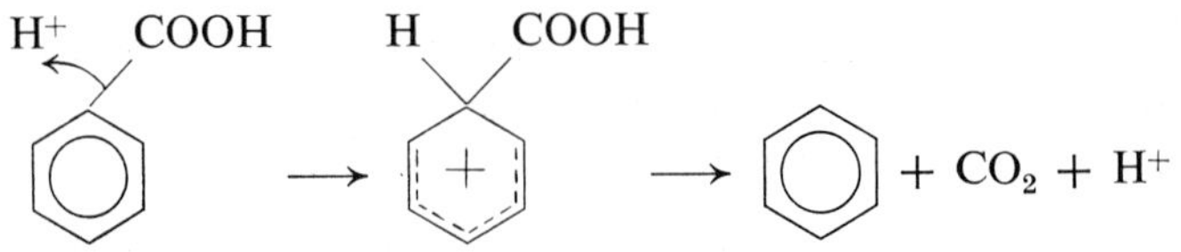

The indole ring is formed by the following reaction:[62]

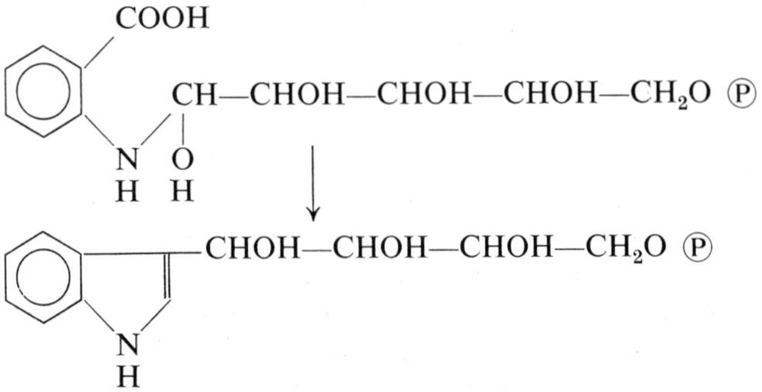

A possible mechanism would be the electrophilic decarboxylation by a carbonium ion.

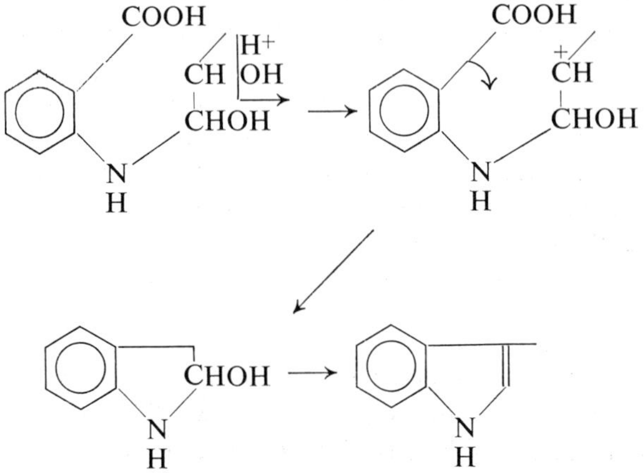

Fatty acid peroxidase catalyzes the reaction between H_2O and a fatty acid to give the next lower aldehyde.[63] A mechanism may be written in

[62] C. Yanofsky, *J. Biol. Chem.* **223**, 171 (1956)
[63] P. K. Stumpf, *J. Biol. Chem.* **223**, 643 (1956)

which the fatty acid is decarboxylated by an electrophilic attack of the peroxidase complex II. Again the positive FeO_2^{2+} ion provides a convenient electron sink for the electron pair.[64] The function of metal ions as acid catalysts in the ionic cleavage of peroxides will be discussed in a later section.

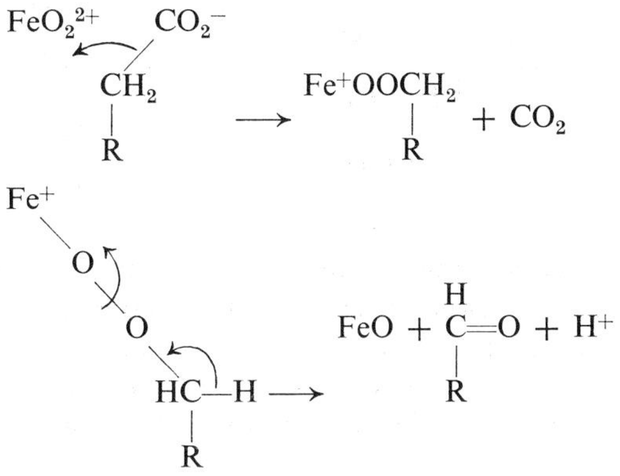

However, peroxidase reactions are known to proceed via free radicals[65] in some reactions and a free radical reaction is certainly a possibility with the fatty acid peroxidase.

Anion removal

Hydride ion. A negative charge formed in a decarboxylation may be disposed of by a simple ionization, such as the ionization of bromide ion in the decarboxylation of dibromocinnamic acid to bromostyrene.[66]

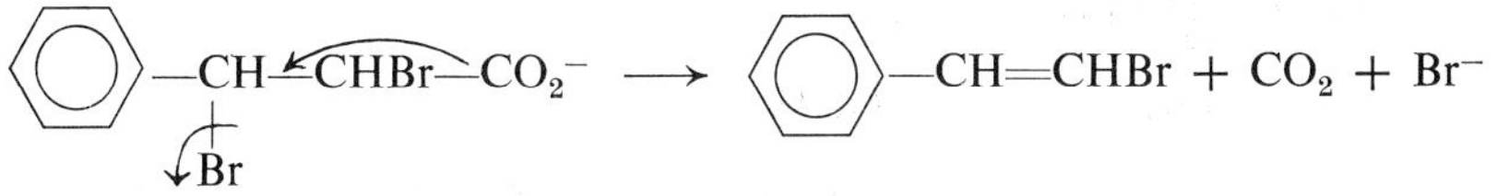

Possibly the oxidative decarboxylation of 6-phosphogluconic acid to ribulose-5-phosphate proceeds via removal of an anion. Oxidation to the β-keto acid followed by a decarboxylation would be expected; however, the β-keto acid has never been observed. If[67] TPN^+ can extract a hydride

[64] R. O. Martin and P. K. Stumpf, *J. Biol. Chem.* **234**, 2548 (1959)

[65] I. Yamazaki, H. S. Mason, and L. Piette, *Biochem. Biophys. Res. Commun.* **1**, 336 (1959)

[66] S. J. Cristol and W. P. Norris, *J. Am. Chem. Soc.* **75**, 632 (1953); E. Grovenstein, Jr. and D. E. Lee, *J. Am. Chem. Soc.* **75**, 2639 (1953); S. J. Cristol and W. P. Norris, *J. Am. Chem. Soc.* **75**, 2645 (1953)

[67] TPN^+ will stand for oxidized triphosphopyridine nucleotide; TPNH for the reduced form; DPN^+ for oxidized diphosphopyridine nucleotide; and DPNH for the reduced form

ion directly from 6-phosphogluconic acid, this may be a way to remove the negative charge formed in decarboxylation similar to the removal of

$$
\begin{array}{ccc}
\text{COOH} & \left[\begin{array}{c}\text{COOH}\end{array}\right] & \text{CH}_2\text{OH} \\
| & | & | \\
\text{HCOH} & \text{HCOH} & \text{C}=\text{O} \\
| & | & | \\
\text{HOCH} \xrightarrow{\text{TPN}^+} & \text{C}=\text{O} & \longrightarrow \quad \text{HCOH} \quad + \text{CO}_2 \\
| & | & | \\
\text{HCOH} & \text{HCOH} & \text{HCOH} \\
| & | & | \\
\text{HCOH} & \text{HCOH} & \text{CH}_2-\text{O}-\circledP \\
| & | & \\
\text{CH}_2-\text{O}-\circledP & \text{CH}_2-\text{O}-\circledP &
\end{array}
$$

bromide ion in the dibromocinnamic acid decarboxylation. Essentially, the TPN$^+$ acts as an electron sink for the electron pair. This type of mechanism would explain why 3-keto-6-phosphogluconic acid has never been detected as an intermediate. A similar mechanism could occur in the oxidative decarboxylation of malic acid to pyruvic acid and isocitric acid

$$
\begin{array}{ccc}
\text{CO}_2^- & \text{HCOH} & \text{H}_2\text{COH} \\
| & \| & | \\
\text{HCOH} & \text{HOC} \quad + \text{CO}_2 + \text{TPNH} \longrightarrow & \text{C}=\text{O} \\
| & | & | \\
\text{HOC}-\text{H TPN}^+ \longrightarrow & &
\end{array}
$$

$$
\begin{array}{cc}
\text{CO}_2^- & \\
| & \text{CH}_3 \\
\text{CH}_2 & | \\
| & \text{C}=\text{O} \\
\text{HO}-\text{C}-\text{H TPN}^+ \longrightarrow & | \\
| & \text{COOH} \\
\text{COOH} &
\end{array}
$$

$$
\begin{array}{cc}
\text{COOH} & \text{COOH} \\
| & | \\
\text{HO}-\text{C}-\text{H TPN}^+ & \text{C}=\text{O} \\
| & | \\
\text{HOOC}-\text{CH} \longrightarrow & \text{CH}_2 \\
| & | \\
\text{CH}_2 & \text{CH}_2 \\
| & | \\
\text{COOH} & \text{COOH}
\end{array}
$$

to α-ketoglutaric acid.[68] If oxalsuccinic acid does occur as an intermediate in this reaction it does not occur as a free intermediate.[69]

[68] W. J. Rutter and H. A. Lardy, *J. Biol. Chem.* **233**, 374 (1958); J. Moyle and M. Dixon, *Biochem. J.* **63**, 548 (1956)

[69] G. Siebert, M. Carsiotis, and G. W. E. Plaut, *J. Biol. Chem.* **977** (1957)

Another similar reaction is the oxidative decarboxylation of prephenic acid by the DPN$^+$ dependent enzyme prephenic dehydrogenase to form p-hydroxyphenyl pyruvic acid.[70] In the decarboxylation of prephenic acid to phenyl pyruvic acid by prephenic aromatase, the anion which leaves could be a hydroxide ion or water. These reactions if concerted would

require that the carboxyl group and the leaving anion are *trans*. It is obvious that both the hydrogen and the hydroxyl can not be *trans* to the carboxyl so that it is likely that only one of these reactions is concerted.

Phosphate ion. The enzymic decarboxylation of mevalonic acid pyrophosphate[71] is another decarboxylation in which an anion leaves. The

[70] I. Schwinck and E. Adams, *Biochim. et Biophys. Acta* **36**, 102 (1959)
[71] K. Bloch, S. Chaykin, A. H. Phillips, and A. De Waard, *J. Biol. Chem.* **234**, 2595 (1959)

requirement for ATP[72] suggests the alcohol is first phosphorylated and the leaving anion is a phosphate ion.

Catalysis by pyridoxal

The decarboxylation of amino acids is catalyzed by enzymes containing pyridoxal phosphate as a cofactor. Pyridoxal will also catalyze the decarboxylation of amino acids in the absence of the enzyme. The pyridoxal forms a Schiff base with amino acid, and the electron-pair formed in the decarboxylation is neutralized by the positive nitrogen of the pyridoxal.[73] The planar intermediate, I, would be expected to give

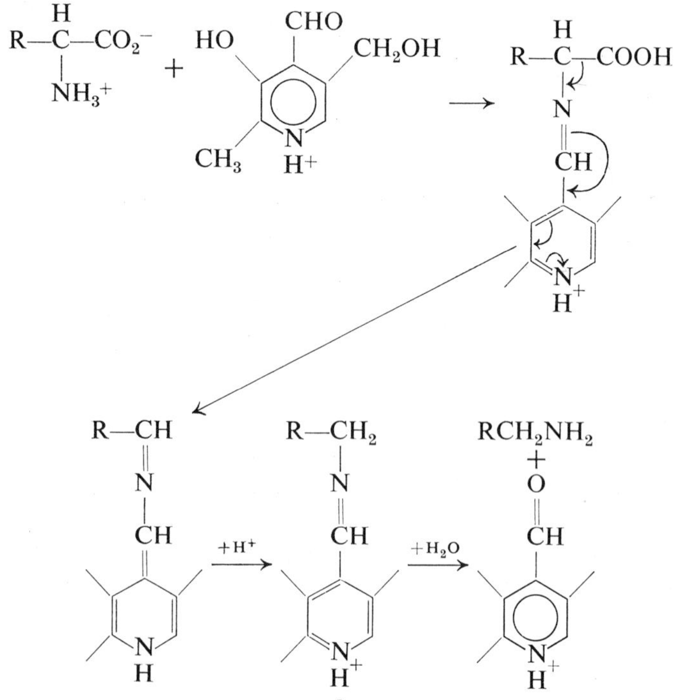

racemized α-deuteroamine in D_2O. However, the decarboxylation proceeds stereospecifically with retention of configuration.[74] The asymmetry of I must be maintained by the enzyme. This is an example of the

[72] Adenosine triphosphate will be abbreviated ATP, adenosine diphosphate, ADP, and adenosine monophosphate, AMP

[73] D. E. Metzler, M. Ikawa, and E. E. Snell, *J. Am. Chem. Soc.* **76**, 648 (1954); S. Mandeles, R. Koppelman, and M. E. Hanke, *J. Biol. Chem.* **209**, 327 (1954)

[74] B. Belleau and J. Burba, *J. Am. Chem. Soc.* **82**, 5751 (1960)

stereospecificity of a nonasymmetric intermediate controlled by an asymmetric environment. Retention of configuration is a characteristic of electrophilic displacement reactions. Possibly the $COOH^+$ is displaced by hydrogen ion and the pyridoxal only serves to stabilize the transition state.

Catalysis by thiamine pyrophosphate

The enzymic decarboxylation of α-keto acids requires thiamine pyrophosphate. The mechanism for this reaction is now known because of the discovery by Mizuhara that thiamine will decarboxylate pyruvate ion in basic solution without an enzyme to produce acetoin.[75] The reactive species of thiazole or thiamine in basic solution is expected to be an anion, because other quaternary ammonium salts will form anions in basic solutions. For example, if the amine I is methylated in basic solution the product is not the quaternary ammonium salt II but the rearranged amine IV. The best explanation is that ion III is formed which can rearrange to give IV. The anion III is made possible by the positive charge on the nitrgoen. This type of an ion is called an ylid.

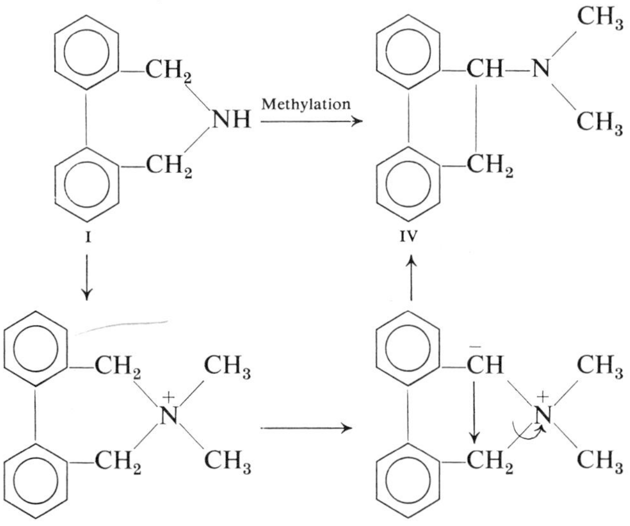

One of the early mechanisms[76] for thiamine action suggested that thiamine forms an anion on the methylene group between the pyrimidine and thiazole rings. However, studies of the decarboxylation catalyzed by thiamine in deuterium oxide showed no incorporation of deuterium on the methylene

[75] S. Mizuhara and P. Handler, *J. Am. Chem. Soc.* **76**, 571 (1954)
[76] K. Wiesner and Z. Valenta, *Experientia* **12**, 190 (1956)

bridge of thiamine.[77] Breslow[78] found that 3,4-dimethylthiazole will also catalyze the decarboxylation of pyruvic acid to give acetoin in basic solution. A study of the nuclear magnetic resonance spectrum of 3,4-dimethyl thiazolium iodide in D_2O showed that the hydrogen in the 2-position of the thiazole ring exchanged with the deuterium[79] of the solvent very rapidly even at pH 7. This means an anion must have been found at the 2-position. If the 2-hydrogen is substituted by a methyl group the thiazolium ion is inactive.[80]

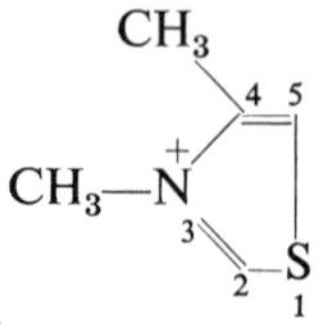

Thiamine can catalyze the decarboxylation of pyruvic acid by first forming the anion analogous to the methyl thiazolium anion.[81] The anion

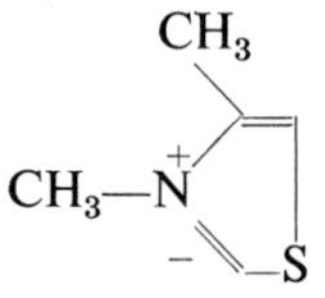

condenses with pyruvic acid; and this product readily decarboxylates

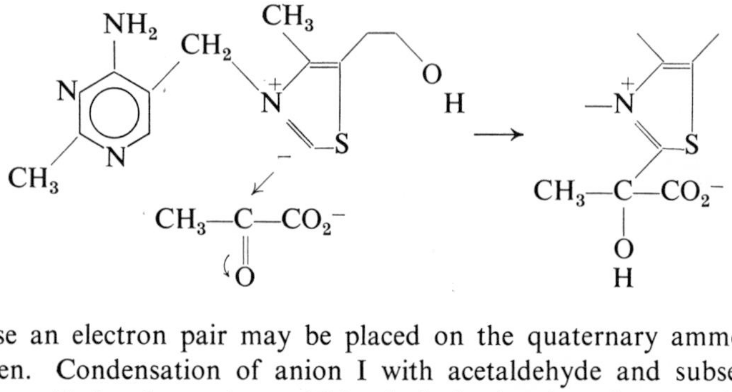

because an electron pair may be placed on the quaternary ammonium nitrogen. Condensation of anion I with acetaldehyde and subsequent cleavage will give the products. Thiazole derivatives have been synthesized

---

[77] L. L. Ingraham and F. H. Westheimer, *Chem. and Ind.* **1956**, 846; K. Fry, L. L. Ingraham, and F. H. Westheimer, *J. Am. Chem. Soc.* **79**, 5225 (1957)

[78] R. Breslow, *Chem. and Ind.* (*B.I.F. Review*) R 28 (1956)

[79] R. Breslow, *J. Am. Chem. Soc.* **79**, 1762 (1957)

[80] J. E. Downes and P. Sykes, *Chem. and Ind.* **1957**, 1095

[81] R. Breslow, *Chem. and Ind.* **1957**, 893

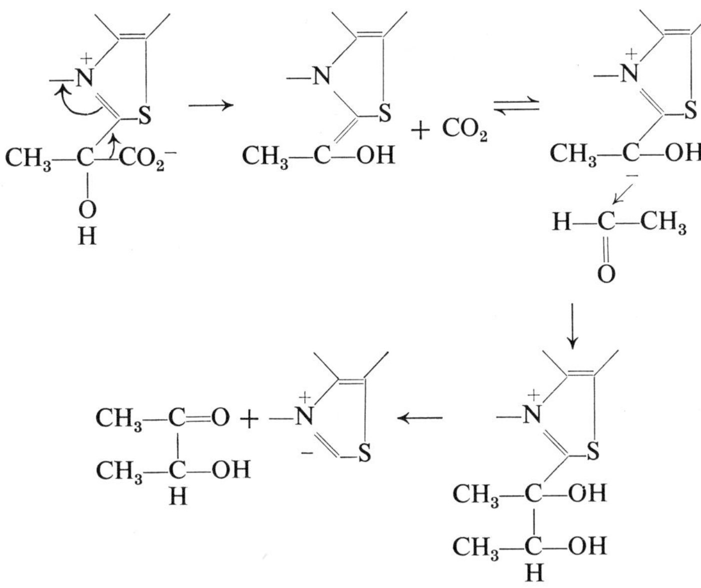

that will give anions analogous to I in basic solution. These compounds have been found to produce acetoin from acetaldehyde with a higher rate

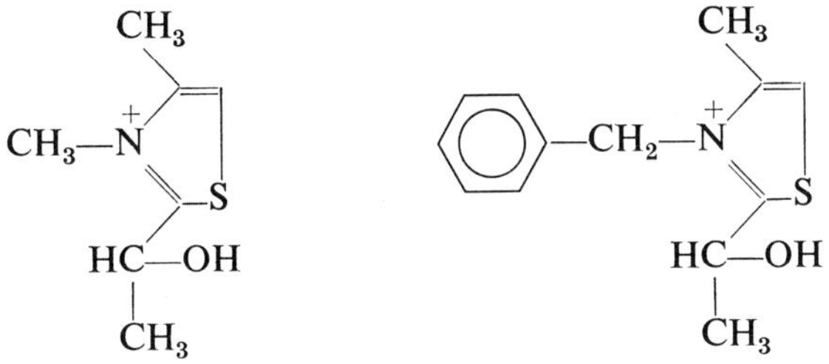

than the parent thiazolium salt. Breslow[82] has pointed out that one of the reasons for this is that the amino group of the pyrimidine ring may aid in forming the thiamine anion.

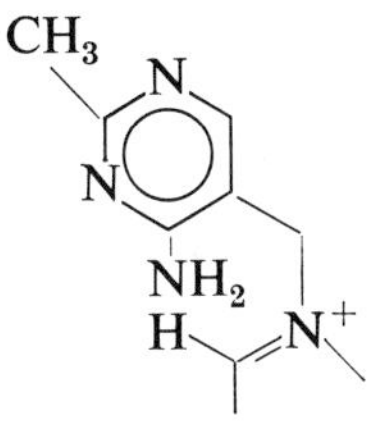

[82] R. Breslow and E. McNelis, *J. Am. Chem. Soc.* **81**, 3080 (1959)

The 2- (α-hydroxyl ethyl) thiamine will substitute for thiamine and phosphoenol pyruvic acid in the reactivation of the enzyme carboxylase.[83]

OXIDATIONS

By oxygen

Nonenzymic. The oxygen molecule is a slow oxidant because the strong bonding between the oxygen atoms must be broken in most oxidation reactions. The oxygen atoms are held together by a single electron pair bond and two three-electron bonds. If two more electrons are added to the molecule in a reduction to form O^{2-} or H_2O_2 the electronic structure becomes isoelectronic with F_2 with one single bond between the atoms. The bond between the oxygen atoms is now easier to break, and reduction by the next two electrons causes bond cleavage. In the reduction of oxygen at an electrode, the oxygen is first reduced to H_2O_2 before the O—O bond is broken.[84]

Catalysis by iron. Ferrous iron and other metals allow a mechanism by which the O—O bond may be broken by the first electron pair reduction. Ferrous iron can combine with oxygen to form FeO_2^{2+}. The FeO_2^{2+} ion, which we shall call perferryl ion, is stabilized by the various ionic resonance forms:

$$FeO_2^{2+}, \qquad Fe^{3+}O_2^{-}, \qquad Fe^{4+}O_2^{2-}$$

Perferryl ion has less bonding between the oxygen atoms than in the oxygen molecule because electrons have been donated to the oxygen from the iron. Reduction by the first pair of electrons may now break the oxygen atoms apart.

Evidence for the existence of a transitory perferryl ion, FeO_2^{2+}, in inorganic chemistry is obtained from studies[85] of the oxidation of ferrous ion by oxygen. The rate expression for the oxidation of ferrous ion by

$$Fe^{2+} + O_2 \rightleftharpoons FeO_2^{2+}$$
$$FeO_2^{2+} + Fe^{2+} + H_2O \longrightarrow Fe^{2+}OOH + Fe^{2+}OH$$

oxygen also contains a term bimolecular in ferrous ion.[86] This term indicates the existence, perhaps only transitory, of a complex of oxygen

---

[83] L. O. Krampitz, G. Gruell, C. S. Miller, J. B. Bicking, H. R. Skeggs, and J. M. Sprague, *J. Am. Chem. Soc.* **80**, 5893 (1958)

[84] W. C. Berl, *Trans. Electrochem. Soc.* **83**, 253 (1943)

[85] P. George, *J. Chem. Soc.* **1954**, 4349

[86] J. Weiss, *Experientia* **9**, 61 (1953); J. Weiss, *Nature* **181**, 825 (1958); P. George, *J. Chem. Soc.* **1954**, 4349; F. E. Huffman and N. Davidson, *J. Am. Chem. Soc.* **78**, 4836 (1956)

with two ferrous ions, such as $Fe^{2+}O_2Fe^{2+}$. The state of oxidation of perferryl ion in enzymes is called Complex III.

Several iron enzymes exist in which the reactive species appears to be perferryl ion. Catechol, for example, is oxidized by oxygen in the presence of pyrocatechase to *cis-cis*-muconic acid with both atoms of the molecular oxygen appearing in the product.[87] Enzymes, of this type, are called

oxygen transferases.[88]

With the weaker bonding between the oxygen atoms in perferryl ion, the first electron pair reduction can break the bond between the oxygen atoms to form ferryl ion, FeO^{2+}. Bray and Gorin postulated the existence of a ferryl ion[89] in inorganic chemistry on the basis of kinetic studies of the reaction of ferric ion with hydrogen peroxide. There is evidence[90] that

$$2Fe^{3+} + H_2O_2 \rightleftharpoons 2Fe^{2+} + FeO^{2+} + H_2O$$

ferryl ion or an ion of this oxidation state may occur in biological systems, because metmyoglobin can be oxidized to a higher oxidation state by either hydrogen peroxide or $IrCl_6^{2-}$. Enzymes in the state of oxidation (4 iron) of ferryl ion are called Complex II.

Peroxidase will hydroxylate salicylic acid by molecular oxygen in the presence of dihydroxyfumaric acid to form 2,3-dihydroxybenzoic acid. The oxygen of the hydroxyl group has been shown to come from oxygen and not from hydrogen peroxide.[91] Possibly perferryl ion formed from oxygen and the peroxidase is reduced by the dihydroxyfumaric acid to ferryl ion and the ferryl ion hydroxylates the salicylic acid. The [OH⁺] ion proposed to initiate the cyclization of squalene to lanosterol could be ferryl ion or a comparable metal ion. The oxygen of the hydroxyl group of lanosterol is derived from the oxygen of the air.[92]

[87] O. Hayaishi, M. Katagiri, and S. Rothberg, *J. Am. Chem. Soc.* **77**, 5450 (1955)
[88] H. S. Mason, *Science* **125**, 1185 (1957)
[89] W. C. Bray and M. H. Gorin, *J. Am. Chem. Soc.* **54**, 2124 (1932)
[90] P. George and D. H. Irvine, *Biochem. J.* **52**, 511 (1952); P. George and D. H. Irvine, *Biochem. J.* **58**, 188 (1954); P. George and D. H. Irvine, *Biochem. J.* **60**, 596 (1955); J. F. Gibson, D. J. E. Ingram, and P. Nicholls, *Nature* **181**, 1398 (1958)
[91] H. S. Mason, I. Onoprienko, and D. Buhler, *Biochim. et Biophys. Acta* **24**, 225 (1957); H. S. Mason, I. Onoprienko, K. Yasunobu, and D. Buhler, *J. Am. Chem. Soc.* **79**, 5578 (1957)
[92] T. T. Tchen and K. Bloch, *J. Biol. Chem.* **226**, 931 (1957)

Ferryl ions or comparable ions may also function in aliphatic hydroxylation reactions. Corey and White[93] have shown that aliphatic compounds are susceptible to electrophilic attack of RO^+. The extension from RO^+ to MO^{2+} is quite easy. The ionization of a hydroperoxide tosylate, will form RO^+ which will attack one of the methyl groups in an electrophilic displacement reaction to form the ether. The enzymic 11-hydroxylation of

$$CH_3\text{---}\underset{CH_3}{\overset{OOH}{\bigcirc}}\text{---}CH_3 + CH_3C_6H_4SO_2Cl \longrightarrow CH_3\text{---}\underset{CH_3}{\overset{O\text{---}SO_2C_6H_4CH_3}{\overset{|}{\underset{\overset{|}{O}}{\bigcirc}}}}\text{---}CH_3$$

$$CH_3\text{---}\underset{CH_3}{\overset{CH_2\text{---}O}{\bigcirc}}\text{---}CH_3 + H^+ \longleftarrow \left[CH_3\text{---}\underset{CH_3}{\overset{CH_3 \quad O^+}{\bigcirc}}\text{---}CH_3 \right]$$

pregnane-3,20-dione[94] proceeds with retention of configuration as would be expected for an electrophilic displacement reaction and requires the reducing agent TPNH.

However, not all hydroxylations proceed by an electrophilic attack of an ion comparable with ferryl ion. The oxygen in the hydroxyl group of 6-hydroxynicotinic acid is derived from water and not from molecular oxygen.[95] Pyridine compounds are notoriously resistant to electrophilic attack.

The ion $FeOOH^{2+}$ is well known in inorganic chemistry from its charge transfer spectra in solutions containing ferric ion and hydrogen peroxide. This ion is comparable with the $FeOH^{2+}$ ion. Enzymes in this state of oxidation (5 iron) are called Complex I.

Chance has shown that catalase reacts with hydrogen peroxide to form Complex I and that Complex I reacts with more hydrogen peroxide to form oxygen and water.[96] This reaction may be another example of an acid-catalyzed hydrogen peroxide oxidation. The transferred group would be a hydride ion. Hydride ion transfer in the rate-determining step is supported by the data of Jarnagin and Wang who showed that the rate in

[93] E. J. Corey and R. W. White, *J. Am. Chem. Soc.* **80**, 6686 (1958); E. J. Corey, G. A. Gregoriou, and D. H. Peterson, *J. Am. Chem. Soc.* **80**, 2338 (1958)

[94] J. K. Grant and A. C. Brownie, *Biochim. et Biophys. Acta* **18**, 433 (1955)

[95] A. L. Hunt, D. E. Hughes, and J. M. Lowenstein, *Biochem. J.* **66**, 2P (1957)

[96] B. Chance and R. R. Ferguson, *Mechanism of Enzyme Action*, edited by W. D. McElroy and B. Glass, Johns Hopkins Press, Baltimore (1954) p. 389

$$\begin{array}{l} \overset{+2}{\underset{}{\text{Fe}}}\overset{}{\text{O}}\overset{}{\cdot}\overset{}{\text{OH}} \\ \quad \overset{}{\text{H}}\big) \\ \quad \overset{\cdots}{\text{O}} \longrightarrow \text{FeO}^+ + \text{H}_2\text{O} + \text{O}_2 + \text{H}^+ \\ \quad \overset{\cdots}{\text{O}}\big) \\ \quad \overset{}{\text{H}} \end{array}$$

H_2O and H_2O_2 was approximately twice[97] the rate in D_2O and D_2O_2. The fact that the O_2 comes from one hydrogen peroxide molecule without reshuffling,[98] and not from the water, gives additional support for this mechanism. Complex I can react also by one-electron oxidations. One-electron oxidations by hydrogen peroxide produce unstable hydroxy radicals.

$$H_2O_2 + e \longrightarrow HO\cdot + {}^-OH$$

If the radical can be stabilized, the reaction will be more likely to occur. Ferric ion is paramagnetic, so it could stabilize the hydroxyl radical formed in the reaction. The product is ferryl ion.

$$Fe^{3+} + \cdot OH \longrightarrow Fe^{3+}OH \longrightarrow FeO^+ + H^+$$

The one-electron oxidation by complex I produces ferryl ion, the stabilized form of a hydroxyl radical, as follows:

$$H^+ + Fe^{2+}OOH + e \longrightarrow FeO^{2+} + H_2O$$

In peroxidase complex I acts as a one-electron oxidant. The most likely mechanism of oxidation of a substrate SH_2 to S via the radical $SH\cdot$ by peroxidase, is through both complexes I and II. The electron paramagnetic

$$Fe^{3+} + H_2O_2 \longrightarrow Fe^{2+}OOH + H^+$$
$$Fe^{2+}OOH + SH_2 \longrightarrow FeO^{2+} + SH\cdot + H_2O$$
$$FeO^{2+} + H^+ + SH_2 \longrightarrow Fe^{3+} + SH\cdot + H_2O$$
$$2SH\cdot \longrightarrow S + SH_2$$

resonance study of peroxidase by Mason and Piette strongly supports this mechanism.

Catalysis by copper. Copper will form complexes comparable to the complexes I, II, and III of the iron enzymes. Probably only two of these, the complexes I and II, occur in the copper enzymes.

Models of Complex I have been studied by Konecny, Havinga, and

[97] R. C. Jarnagin and J. H. Wang, *J. Am. Chem. Soc.* **80**, 6477 (1958)
[98] R. C. Jarnagin and J. H. Wang, *J. Am. Chem. Soc.* **80**, 786 (1958); M. Dole, D. P. Rudd, G. R. Muchow, and C. Comte, *J. Chem. Phys.* **20**, 961 (1952)

others.[99] For example, Konecny has found that hydrogen peroxide and cupric ion will hydroxylate benzene and sodium benzoate to phenol and salicylic acid. Havinga and co-workers have studied the copper-catalyzed hydroxylation of phenols and aniline in the presence of amines. This model system is similar to the enzyme, tyrosinase, in two important respects. Both the model system and tyrosinase contain copper and both hydroxylate in the ortho position. Brackman and Havinga proposed a mechanism[100] in which the oxidant is hydrogen peroxide, formed by subsequent oxidation of some of the oxidation products. Cupric ion, phenol, and hydrogen peroxide form a complex comparable to complex I of the iron enzymes which directs the hydroxylation in the ortho position. Cupric ion effectively acts as an acid catalyst which polarizes the oxygen-oxygen bond so that it will cleave ionically with the electron pair remaining on the oxygen near the copper. The resulting OH^+ fragment hydroxylates

the benzene ring in a typical electrophilic displacement reaction. Copper in this reaction acts in the same way as two protons in other acid-catalyzed hydrogen peroxide oxidations.[101]

Complex I of copper can also react in a free radical reaction comparable to complex I of the iron enzymes. In this manner copper can aid a one-electron reduction of hydrogen peroxide by stabilizing the resulting hydroxyl radical as CuO^+.

$$Cu^+OOH + e \rightarrow CuO^+ + H^+$$

An example of a one-electron reduction[102] of hydrogen peroxide occurs in the oxidation of catechol to the semiquinone by cupric ion and hydrogen peroxide.

Cupryl ion or CuO^+ is comparable to complex II of the iron enzymes.

[99] J. O. Konecny, *J. Am. Chem. Soc.* **76**, 4993 (1954); W. Brackman and E. Havinga, *Rec. trav. chim.* **74**, 1021, 1070 (1955); G. Engelsma and E. Havinga, *Tetrahedron* **2**, 289 (1957)

[100] W. Brackman and E. Havinga, *Rec. trav. chim.* **74**, 1100, 1107 (1955)

[101] J. O. Edwards, *J. Phys. Chem.* **56**, (1952); M. Anbar and H. Taube, *J. Am. Chem. Soc.* **76**, 6243 (1954)

[102] L. L. Ingraham, *Arch. Biochem. Biophys.* **81**, 309 (1959)

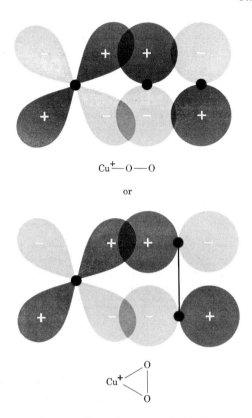

$$Cu^{+}\!\!-O-O$$

or

$$Cu^{+}\!\!\diagdown\!\!\genfrac{}{}{0pt}{}{O}{O}$$

This ion is a strong electrophile and very probably is responsible for some electrophilic hydroxylations.

Percupryl, CuO_2^+, is the copper analog of complex III of the iron enzymes. The copper of the enzyme tyrosinase exists as cuprous ion[103] so that percupryl ion is probably formed by a direct reaction between the cuprous enzyme and molecular oxygen. Tyrosinase and hemocyanin, which carries oxygen like hemoglobin, both contain two cuprous ions for each oxygen absorbed. Complex III is therefore probably $Cu^+O_2Cu^+$ but the arguments below hold for both CuO_2^+ and $Cu^+O_2Cu^+$. Percupryl ion is stabilized by donation of electrons from the $3d\pi$ orbital of the cuprous ion to the $2p$ orbitals of the oxygen. This extra bonding in addition to the $sp^3\sigma$ bonding of the cuprous ion forms a double bond between the copper and oxygen. All the $3d$ orbitals of cuprous ion are filled so that the $4s$ and $4p$ orbitals are used for chelation. These orbitals hydridize to form sp^3 tetrahedral bonds. The $3d\pi$ orbitals lie at a higher energy level in a

[103] D. Kertez, *Nature* **180**, 506 (1956)

tetrahedral field (cf. section on ligand field theory) so that the electrons in these orbitals are more readily donated to the oxygen. One of the functions of the protein in tyrosinase and other oxygen-carrying copper enzymes must be to form a tetrahedral field around the copper. Donation of electrons to oxygen would allow resonance forms with negative charges on oxygen.[104] Forms with two positive charges on copper do not indicate

$$Cu^+O_2Cu^+, \qquad Cu^{2+}O_2{}^-Cu^+, \qquad Cu^{2+}O_2{}^{2-}Cu^{2+}$$

paramagnetism because the electron on the copper and on the oxygen are still paired and so form a bond. Resonance between diamagnetic and paramagnetic states is not allowed. Oxygenated hemocyanin is diamagnetic.[105]

Similar structural arguments apply for the cupryl ion. Mechanisms including these last two complexes, II and III, may be written for tyrosinase. This enzyme is a "mixed function oxidase," *i.e.*, only one of the oxygen atoms of molecular oxygen is transferred to a substrate.[106] When tyrosinase hydroxylates 3,4-dimethyl phenol to form 4,5-dimethyl catechol, the oxygen of the hydroxyl group comes from molecular oxygen and not from water.[107] These results are in agreement with a mechanism in which complex III is formed from the cuprous enzyme and oxygen, the complex III is reduced to complex II, and complex II hydroxylates the benzene ring. Indirect evidence[108] for the existence of cupryl ion in tyrosinase is obtained

$$Cu^+ + O_2 \overset{1}{\rightleftharpoons} CuO_2{}^+ \quad \text{or} \quad Cu^+O_2Cu^+$$

$$CuO_2{}^+ + 2e + 2H^+ \overset{2}{\longrightarrow} CuO^+ + H_2O$$

$$CuO^+ + \varphi H \overset{3}{\longrightarrow} \varphi OCu^+ + H^+$$

$$\varphi OCu^+ + H^+ \overset{4}{\longrightarrow} \varphi OH + Cu^+$$

from a study of the denaturation of the enzyme in acid and from kinetic studies.

Although the nitration of benzene does not show a tritium rate effect[109] (cf. section on electrophilic substitutions), other electrophilic attacks on the benzene ring do show such effects,[110] which commonly occur when a

[104] R. J. P. Williams, *Biol. Rev.* **28**, 381 (1953); I. M. Klotz and T. A. Klotz, *Science* **121**, 477 (1955); R. J. P. Williams, *Science* **122**, 558 (1955)

[105] T. Nakamura and H. S. Mason, *Biochem. Biophys. Res. Commun.* **3**, 297 (1960)

[106] H. S. Mason, *Nature* **177**, 79 (1956)

[107] H. S. Mason, W. L. Fowlks, and E. Peterson, *J. Am. Chem. Soc.* **77**, 2914 (1955)

[108] L. L. Ingraham, *Pigment Cell Biology*, edited by Myron Gordon, Academic Press Inc., New York (1959) p. 609; L. L. Ingraham, *J. Am. Chem. Soc.* **79**, 666 (1957)

[109] L. Melander, *Acta Chem. Scand.* **3**, 95 (1949)

[110] S. Olsson, *Arkiv Kemi* **14**, 85 (1959); E. Shilov and F. Weinstein, *Nature* **182**, 1300 (1958)

powerful electrophile attacks an easily substituted aromatic compound. The mechanism proposed above for the attack of CuO^+ on a phenol to form a catechol (Reaction 3) might be expected to show a tritium effect because CuO^+ is a powerful electrophile and a phenol is easily attacked. The enzymic hydroxylation shows a very small (about 5 per cent) rate effect.[111] This result was obtained by allowing the enzyme to act on partially tritiated phenol and observing that after partial reaction the unreacted phenol was enriched in tritium. A tritium rate effect indicates the second step of the substitution must be rate-determining because the

carbon-tritium bond is broken in this step. The smallness of the rate effect indicates that the tritium does not ionize off but is pulled off very efficiently by a base on the enzyme. These results do not rule out a radical reaction because radical attacks[112] on benzene also show small tritium rate effects.

However, not all copper enzymes proceed through complexes II and III. Laccase and perhaps ascorbic acid oxidase operate through a cuprous-cupric couple. Both spectral and magnetic susceptibility measurements give evidence[113] for a cuprous-cupric couple in laccase. By a spectral study of the cupric form of the enzyme the stoichiometry of the laccase-catalyzed oxidation of hydroquinone was found[114] to follow the equations below:

$$2Cu^{2+} + \text{Hydroquinone} \longrightarrow 2Cu^+ + \text{Quinone}$$
$$2Cu^+ + \tfrac{1}{2}O_2 \longrightarrow 2Cu^{2+} + H_2O$$

An intermediate semiquinone has been detected in this reaction by means of electron paramagnetic resonance studies.[115]

Enzymes not containing metals. The enzyme lipoxidase is of particular interest because it catalyzes oxidations by molecular oxygen but contains no metals. The nonenzymic oxidation of linoleic acid by oxygen proceeds by chain reaction.

[111] B. J. B. Wood and L. L. Ingraham (Unpublished results)
[112] E. L. Eliel, Z. Welwart, and S. H. Wilen, *J. Org. Chem.* **23**, 1821 (1958)
[113] T. Nakamura, *Biochim. et Biophys. Acta* **30**, 44, 538 (1958); B. G. Malmstrom, R. Mosbach, and T. Vanngard, *Nature* **183**, 321 (1959)
[114] T. Nakamura, *Biochim. et Biophys. Acta* **30**, 538 (1958)
[115] T. Nakamura, *Biochim. Biophys. Res. Commun.* **2**, 111 (1960)

$$RH + O_2 \xrightarrow{1} R\cdot + HO_2\cdot$$

$$R\cdot + O_2 \xrightarrow{2} RO_2\cdot$$

$$RO_2\cdot + RH \xrightarrow{3} RO_2H + R\cdot$$

$$2R\cdot \xrightarrow{4} R\!-\!R$$

The slowness of reaction 1 compared with reactions 2 and 3 produces an induction period in the nonenzymic reaction. However, the lipoxidase-catalyzed reaction has been reported not to have an induction period. These results were explained by assuming the following two reactions to occur on the enzyme surface so that free radicals were never free in solution.[116] Recent results[117] have shown that an induction period may

$$RH + O_2 \longrightarrow R\cdot + \cdot O_2H \longrightarrow RO_2H$$

be observed with lipoxidase if the substrates are extremely pure. The induction period can be eliminated by the addition of linoleic peroxide. The hydroperoxide of the linoleic acid forms on the methylene group between the two double bonds. This position is the most susceptible

$$-CH\!=\!CH\!-\!CH\!-\!CH\!=\!CH-$$
$$\overset{|}{O}$$
$$O$$
$$H$$

to oxidation because the radical first formed is stabilized by resonance. In order for this type of resonance to occur, the p orbitals on the methylene

Lowest molecular orbital

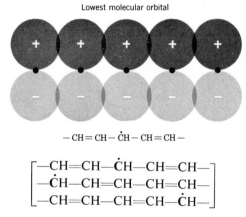

$$-CH\!=\!CH\!-\!\overset{\cdot}{C}H\!-\!CH\!=\!CH-$$

$$\begin{bmatrix} -CH\!=\!CH\!-\!\overset{\cdot}{C}H\!-\!CH\!=\!CH- \\ -\overset{\cdot}{C}H\!-\!CH\!=\!CH\!-\!CH\!=\!CH- \\ -CH\!=\!CH\!-\!CH\!=\!CH\!-\!\overset{\cdot}{C}H- \end{bmatrix}$$

[116] A. L. Tappel, P. D. Boyer, and W. O. Lundberg, *J. Biol. Chem.* **199**, 267 (1952)
[117] J. L. Haining and B. Axelrod, *J. Biol. Chem.* **232**, 193 (1958)

group must be held in the proper position to overlap with the p orbitals of the double bond. Holding these orbitals in the proper position may be one of the important functions of lipoxidase.

By flavins

The oxidation or reduction of flavins is a two-electron reaction which can proceed by two one-electron reactions through an intermediate semiquinone. This semiquinone may be stabilized by (1) resonance; (2) complexing with metal; or perhaps (3) complexing with an aromatic ring.

The semiquinone is an important type of free radical which is stabilized by resonance. The odd electron on the oxygen or nitrogen of a semiquinone is in a p orbital parallel to the p orbitals of an aromatic group. Overlap between these p orbitals forms a large orbital which allows the free electron to spread out over a large area thus adding stability to the radical. The details of structure and resonance of semiquinones is well reviewed in the papers of Michaelis.[118]

Complexing with metals will also stabilize free radicals. Many metallic ions contain an odd electron which can pair with the odd electron of the free radical or they can accommodate an odd electron in their orbitals easily. For example, the ferryl iron,[119] FeO^{2+}, and cupryl ion,[120] CuO^+, discussed in the last chapter, may be thought of as hydroxyl radicals stabilized by ferric and cupric ions.

$$Fe^{3+} + \cdot OH \longrightarrow FeO^{2+} + H^+$$
$$Cu^{2+} + \cdot OH \longrightarrow CuO^+ + H^+$$

Metals stabilize organic free radicals in a similar manner. By stabilizing radicals metals can control the products formed in a free radical reaction. The decomposition of t-butyl peroxide gives the unstable t-butoxy radicals which subsequently decompose to methyl radicals and acetone. Seldom are products of t-butoxy radicals formed. For example, the thermal decomposition of t-butyl peroxide in benzaldehyde produces benzpinacol dibenzoate[121] which must have been formed from radicals resulting from

$$CH_3-\overset{\overset{\displaystyle CH_3}{|}}{\underset{\underset{\displaystyle CH_3}{|}}{C}}-O-O-\overset{\overset{\displaystyle CH_3}{|}}{\underset{\underset{\displaystyle CH_3}{|}}{C}}-CH_3 \longrightarrow 2CH_3-\overset{\overset{\displaystyle CH_3}{|}}{\underset{\underset{\displaystyle CH_3}{|}}{C}}-O\cdot \longrightarrow \overset{\overset{\displaystyle CH_3}{|}}{\underset{\underset{\displaystyle CH_3}{|}}{C}}=O + CH_3\cdot$$

[118] L. Michaelis, in *The Enzymes*, edited by J. B. Sumner and K. Myrbach, Academic Press, New York (1951); L. Michaelis, *Chem. Rev.* **16**, 243 (1935)
[119] W. C. Bray and M. H. Gorin, *J. Am. Chem. Soc.* **54**, 2124 (1932)
[120] L. L. Ingraham, *Arch. Biochem. Biophys.* **81**, 309–318 (1959)
[121] M. S. Karasch and A. Fono, *J. Org. Chem.* **23**, 324 (1958)

the action of methyl radicals on benzaldehyde. However, if cupric ion is added the primary product is *t*-butyl benzoate, which must have been derived from a *t*-butoxy radical. Stabilization with cupric ion prevented

Without Cu^{2+}

With Cu^{2+}

the decomposition of the *t*-butoxy radical. A metal ion can similarily stabilize the intermediate semiquinone in flavin oxidations and reductions.[122]

Mahler and Green[123] have discussed the importance of metals for one-electron oxidation in flavin enzymes. These authors point out that the reduced form of flavin adenine dinucleotide (FAD) may have semiquinone character in the presence of one of two metal ions. This means that the semiquinone (FADH) of FAD may be stabilized by the two metal ions, M^{n+}.

$$M^{n+}\overset{+}{\text{---}}FADH_2\text{---}M^{n+}, M^{n+}\text{---}FADH_2\text{---}M^{(n+1)+}, M^{(n-1)+}\text{---}FADH_2^{2+}\text{---}M^{n+}$$

Free radicals are also probably stabilized by complexing with aromatic compounds. This stabilization may occur through $2p\sigma$ bonds.[124] For example, in the reaction of chlorine atoms with 2,3 dimethyl butane, about 3.5 times as much tertiary chloride as primary chloride is formed when the reaction occurs in aliphatic solvents. However, in aromatic solvents where complexing is possible, the reaction is much more selective, and as much as twenty-four times the quantity of tertiary chloride is formed.[125] Similar radical aromatic complexes have been postulated by Mayo and Hammond.[126] There is no evidence for any similar type of complexing in enzymic reactions but the possibility certainly exists.

[122] D. J. D. Nicholas, *Nature* **179**, 800 (1957)

[123] H. R. Mahler and D. E. Green, *Science* **120**, 7 (1954); H. R. Mahler, A. S. Fairhurst and B. Mackler, *J. Am. Chem. Soc.* **77**, 1514 (1955)

[124] L. L. Ingraham, *J. Chem. Phys.* **18**, 988 (1950)

[125] G. A. Russell, *J. Am. Chem. Soc.* **79**, 2977 (1957)

[126] F. R. Mayo, *J. Am. Chem. Soc.* **75**, 6133 (1953); G. S. Hammond, C. E. Boozer, C. E. Hamilton, and J. N. Sen., *J. Am. Chem. Soc.* **77**, 3238 (1955)

A flavin may therefore react with either a two-electron oxidation-reduction couple or with a one-electron oxidation-reduction couple. Compounds that can act as both one-electron or two-electron systems will catalyze reactions which are slow because of the "Equivalence Change Principle."

This principle, first proposed by Shaffer,[127] states that if both oxidant and reductant can undergo the same number of electron changes, the reaction is fast; if the number differs, the reaction is slow. For example, ceric ion gains one electron in oxidations and thallous ion loses two electrons, and these ions react slowly. Many two-electron oxidations react very rapidly if Shaffer's principle is obeyed.[128]

The flavins could thus act as catalysts by coupling one-electron reactions to two-electron reactions. The flavins would act as one-electron systems to the cytochromes and as a two-electron system to DPNH. Model reactions have shown that pyridine nucleotide analogs probably react with flavins by two-electron reactions.[129] In model systems, flavins have been shown to act as catalysts between one-electron and two-electron reactions. For example, flavins strongly catalyze the reaction between the one-electron reductant titanous ion and the two-electron oxidant iodine.[130]

Johnson and Winstein[131] have investigated this problem more thoroughly and have found that many compounds that can form semiquinones will act as powerful catalysts in the titanous iodine reaction. For example, 2-hydroxy-3-amino phenazine at a concentration of 10^{-7} moles per liter will increase the rate over the uncatalyzed rate of reaction by a factor of three. Phenazines are also highly effective nonphysiological catalysts in coupling one-electron systems to two-electron systems in cyclic photosynthetic phosphorylation.

By cytochromes

The Franck-Condon principle is an important factor[132] in electron transfer reactions. Usually referred to in discussions of spectroscopy, this states that electron movements are instantaneous compared with movements of atoms. This means that electron transfer in oxidation-reduction reactions occurs much faster than reorganization of a complex ion, and the rate depends upon the rate of reorganization. If a large reorganization is required before electron transfer can occur the reaction will be slow.

[127] P. A. Shaffer, *J. Am. Chem. Soc.* **55**, 2169 (1933)
[128] A. E. Remick, *J. Am. Chem. Soc.* **69**, 94 (1947)
[129] C. H. Suelter and D. E. Metzler, *Biochim. et Biophys. Acta* **44**, 23 (1960)
[130] P. A. Shaffer, *J. Phys. Chem.* **40**, 1021 (1936)
[131] C. E. Johnson and S. Winstein, *J. Am. Chem. Soc.* **74**, 755 (1952)
[132] B. J. Zwolinski, R. J. Marcus, and H. Eyring, *Chem. Rev.* **55**, 157 (1955)

For example, MnO_4^{2-} and MnO_4^- have similar structures and the reaction between these ions is fast, but AsO_4^{3-} and AsO_3^{3-} have dissimilar structures and the reaction between them is slow. A ferric ion holds its water of hydration much closer than does a ferrous ion. When an electron transfer between ferrous ion and ferric ion in aqueous solution occurs, a large reorganization of the hydration shell is required and the reaction proceeds comparatively slowly. However, if the iron is chelated in a rigid porphyrin the change in hydration must be very small and the reaction comparatively fast. This may be one of the functions of the porphyrins in the cytochromes.[133]

The oxidation-reduction potential of iron compounds is determined by the energy of the electrons in the $3d$ orbitals. The energy of these electrons is determined by the field around the iron (cf. ligand field theory). The $3d_{z^2}$ orbital in particular is important because ferrous ion has six $3d$ electrons and ferric ion has five $3d$ electrons. The extra electron when in an octahedral field such as the cytochromes is added to the $3d_{z^2}$ orbital (cf. $3d$ splittings in an octahedral field). The energy of the $3d_{z^2}$ orbital is determined by the distance to the group on the z axis which is determined by the protein. The protein may therefore control the oxidation-reduction potential of the cytochromes. Possibly changes in protein structure during some process may change the potentials of the cytochromes.

By pyridine nucleotides

Oxidations by DPN^+ have been shown to take place by direct hydrogen transfer[134] from substrate to DPN^+. Such a transfer could occur by (1) a hydride ion transfer, (2) a hydrogen atom transfer, or (3) a hydrogen atom transfer in a charge transfer complex of the pyridine nucleotide and substrate.

Hydride ion transfers have been observed in many nonenzymatic oxidation-reduction reactions. For example, the reduction of phenyl diazonium ion by ethyl alcohol[135] to give benzene, nitrogen, and acetaldehyde has been considered to proceed via a hydride transfer. This reaction can be thought of as a model of the alcohol dehydrogenase reaction.

The reduction of diphenylcarbinol to diphenylmethane by isopropanol in sulfuric acid has been shown to occur via a direct hydrogen transfer. This reaction appears to be a hydride transfer mechanism.[136]

---

[133] J. Weiss, *Proc. Roy. Soc.* A **222**, 128 (1954)

[134] F. H. Westheimer, H. F. Fisher, E. E. Conn, and B. Vennesland, *J. Am. Chem. Soc.* **73**, 2403 (1951)

[135] N. C. Deno, H. J. Peterson, and G. S. Saines, *Chem. Rev.* **60**, 7 (1960)

[136] P. D. Bartlett and J. D. McCollum, *J. Am. Chem. Soc.* **78**, 1441 (1956)

$$\begin{array}{c}\phi \\ \diagdown \\ \diagup \\ \phi \end{array}\!\!CHOH + H^+ \longrightarrow \begin{array}{c}\phi \\ \diagdown \\ \diagup \\ \phi \end{array}\!\!CH^+ + H_2O$$

$$\begin{array}{c}\phi \\ \diagdown \\ \diagup \\ \phi \end{array}\!\!CH^+ + D{-}\!\!\overset{\displaystyle CH_3}{\underset{\displaystyle CH_3}{\overset{|}{\underset{|}{C}}}}\!\!{-}OH \longrightarrow \begin{array}{c}\phi \\ \diagdown \\ \diagup \\ \phi \end{array}\!\!CHD + \overset{\displaystyle CH_3}{\underset{\displaystyle CH_3}{\overset{|}{\underset{|}{C}}}}\!\!{=}O + H^+$$

Triphenyl carbonium ion, used in the form of its perchlorate salt, is an interesting oxidizing agent. This ion very probably oxidizes substrates by the removal of a hydride ion. It will oxidize 9,10-dihydroanthracene to anthracene and xanthen to xanthylium ion.[137]

Xanthen   Xantlylium ion

Triphenyl carbonium ion will oxidize formic acid to carbon dioxide by direct deuterium transfer.[138]

Similarily the reduction of a ketone by a secondary alcohol catalyzed by sodium alkoxide has also been shown to occur by a direct hydrogen transfer.[139] The reaction is unaffected by free radical inhibitors and thus appears to be a hydride transfer.

Westheimer and co-workers have studied model reactions much closer to the enzymic reaction. Malachite green can be reduced by N-benzyl dihydronicotinamide.[140] The hydrogen is transferred directly from nicotinamide to dye in this reaction also. The transfer is probably a hydride ion because of the positive nature of the receptor, but it could be a hydrogen atom.

The same nicotinamide will also reduce thiobenzophenone to the mercaptan.[141] This reaction again involves a direct hydrogen transfer. Electron-donating groups (*p*-hydroxy, *o*-methoxy, and *p*-methoxy) on the thiobenzophenone decrease the reaction rate, and an electron-withdrawing

[137] W. Bonthrone and D. H. Reid, *J. Chem. Soc.* **1959**, 2773
[138] R. Stewart, *Can. J. Chem.* **35**, 766 (1957)
[139] W. von E. Doering and T. C. Aschner, *J. Am. Chem. Soc.* **75**, 393 (1953)
[140] O. Mauzerall and F. H. Westheimer, *J. Am. Chem. Soc.* **77**, 2261 (1951)
[141] R. H. Abeles, R. F. Hutton, and F. H. Westheimer, *J. Am. Chem. Soc.* **79**, 712 (1957)

group increases the rate. These results are to be expected if a hydride ion is transferred to the thiobenzophenone in the rate-determining step, which is a type of hydrogen transfer because hydrogen is transferred faster than deuterium. The reaction is unaffected by oxygen or free-radical inhibitors.

The discussion of flavins showed that flavins might react with cytochromes by one-electron oxidation-reductions, and with the pyridine nucleotides by two-electron reactions. Suelter and Metzler[142] studied the reaction of N-propyl dihydronicotinamide with riboflavin. The reaction will not occur if the riboflavin is an anion, and the cation of riboflavin will react 104 times as fast as the neutral riboflavin. These results are consistent with a hydride removal by the riboflavin—a two-electron reaction. The reaction shows an isotope effect with deuterium. The rate acts like the rate of a reaction producing ions: increasing with an increase in ionic strength, and decreasing with a decrease in dielectric constant.

[142] C. H. Suelter and D. E. Metzler, *Biochim. et Biophys. Acta* **44**, 23 (1960)

Zinc occurs in alcohol dehydrogenase. It has been considered to function as an acid catalyst,[143] complexing with the carbonyl of the acetaldehyde and aiding in the removal of a hydride ion from DPNH.

$$H \quad H\text{------}\underset{\underset{CH_3}{|}}{\overset{\overset{H}{|}}{C}}\text{=}O\text{------}Zn^{2+}$$

Evidence seems to be increasing to show that the DPN^+ oxidation of alcohol does not proceed by a hydrogen atom transfer. Mahler[144] has searched very carefully for free radicals in the DPN^+ alcohol reaction by means of electron paramagnetic resonance and has not been able to detect radicals.

The pyridine nucleotide could form a charge transfer complex in which an electron is transferred from substrate to the nucleotide followed by a hydrogen atom transfer. This type of mechanism has been pointed out by Kosower and Weiss.[145] Charge transfer complexes require little electron transfer from donor to acceptor molecules in the ground state and usually the amount of transfer is very small. A mechanism in which 1/100th of an electron is transferred followed by a hydrogen atom with the remaining 99 per cent of the electron is effectively a hydride ion transfer. Charge transfer mechanisms merge imperceptibly with hydride ion transfer mechanisms. A charge transfer mechanism would be favored if the substrate were bound to the enzyme DPN^+ complex more strongly than the substrate would be bound to the enzyme alone. This binding order agrees with the observed enzyme kinetics.[146]

By lipoic acid

Lipoic acid, also called thioctic acid, is strained because of electron repulsions between the filled p_z orbitals in sulfur. In a cyclic disulfide these

[143] K. Wallenfels and H. Sund, *Biochem. Z.* **329**, 59 (1957)

[144] H. R. Mahler, *Symposium on Free Radicals in Biological Systems*, Stanford Biophysics Laboratory, March 21–23 (1960)

[145] E. M. Kosower, *J. Am. Chem. Soc.* **77**, 3883 (1955); E. M. Kosower and P. E. Klinedinst, *J. Am. Chem. Soc.* **78**, 3493 (1956); E. M. Kosower, *J. Am. Chem. Soc.* **78**, 3497 (1956); J. Weiss, *Nature* **181**, 825 (1958)

[146] H. Theorell, A. P. Nygaard, and R. Bonnichsen, *Acta Chem. Scand.* **9**, 1148 (1955); K. Wallenfels and H. Schuly, *Biochem. Z.* **329**, 75 (1957)

$$\begin{array}{c} \text{S---S} \\ \diagup \quad \diagdown \\ \text{CH}_2 \qquad \text{CH---CH}_2\text{---CH}_2\text{---CH}_2\text{---CH}_2\text{---COOH} \\ \diagdown \quad \diagup \\ \text{CH}_2 \end{array}$$

orbitals both containing two electrons will be parallel, thereby giving a maximum repulsion between them. In an open chain disulfide the sulfur-sulfur bond is able to rotate, so that the orbitals orient at 90° to each other to minimize the repulsion between them. The electronic strain in lipoic acid causes the disulfide bond to cleave easily to the open form.

A more sophisticated explanation[147] of the electronic strain in lipoic acid states that the $3p_z$ orbitals may add and subtract to make two new π orbitals when the orbitals are parallel and the angle between the R groups

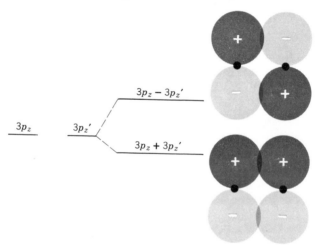

is zero. The two electrons in the higher orbital are destabilized more than electrons in the lower orbital are stabilized so that the overall effect is a destabilization. The excited state of lipoic acid is more stable with splitting than without. When an electron is excited to a higher orbital than the three remaining electrons, two are stabilized and only one is destabilized on splitting, thus resulting in a more stable state. As the angle between the R groups increases through various disulfides to 90° the interaction between the orbitals decreases and the splitting decreases. The energy between the ground and excited state is less for $\theta = 0°$ than for $\theta = 90°$ so that lipoic acid will absorb at longer wave lengths than an open chain disulfide.[148]

[147] G. Bergson, *Arkiv Kemi* **12**, 233 (1958)
[148] J. A. Barltrop, P. M. Hayes, and M. Calvin, *J. Am. Chem. Soc.* **76**, 4348 (1954)

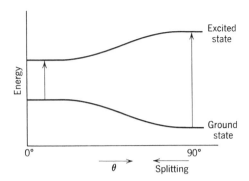

Lipoic acid can oxidize a substance X to XOH or reduce XOH to X through two nucleophilic displacement reactions. These are efficient mechanisms for oxidation or reduction because nucleophic displacement

$$X \longrightarrow S \overset{\curvearrowright}{} S \rightleftharpoons X-S \quad S^- \longrightarrow X-S \quad \overset{H}{S}$$

$$H_2O \longrightarrow X \overset{\curvearrowright}{} \overset{H}{S} \quad \rightleftharpoons HOX + \overset{H}{S} \quad \overset{H}{S}$$

reactions by, on, or of sulfur are fast reactions (cf. section on displacement reactions).

An example of the forward reaction occurs in the decarboxylation and oxidation of pyruvic acid to acetyl coenzyme A.[149] If the anion formed in

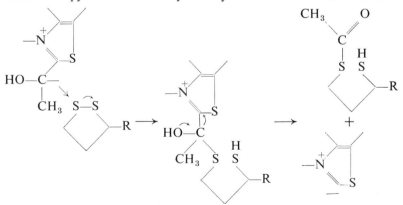

[149] L. J. Reed and B. G. DeBusk, *J. Am. Chem. Soc.* **75,** 1261 (1953); L. J. Reed, *Physiol. Rev.* **33,** 544 (1953)

the decarboxylation of pyruvic acid (cf. section on decarboxylation) attacks oxidized lipoic acid in a nucleophilic displacement reaction followed by a reverse condensation, the products will be acetyl lipoate and thiamine. In this manner the acetaldehyde could be oxidized to the oxidation state of acetic acid. Displacement of the lipoic acid by coenzyme A would produce acetyl coenzyme A and reduce lipoic acid.

An example of the reverse reaction occurs in the reduction of sulfate ion to sulfite ion by reduced lipoic acid. However, the sulfate ion must be first "activated" before attack by the reduced lipoic acid is possible. Two molecules of ATP react with one of the sulfate ion to give 3'-phospho-adenosine-5'-phosphosulfate (PAPS). Reduced lipoic acid is now able to attack the sulfate to form a lipothiosulfate and 3'-phospho-AMP.

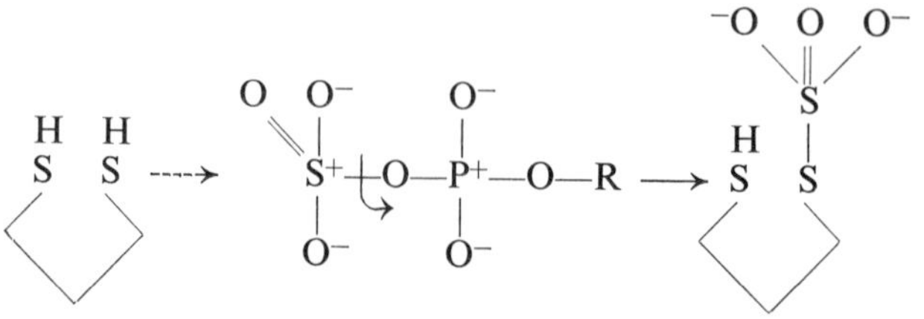

Nucleophilic attack by the other sulfhydryl group will form oxidized lipoic acid and sulfite ion.[150] Nucleophilic attacks on the divalent sulfur

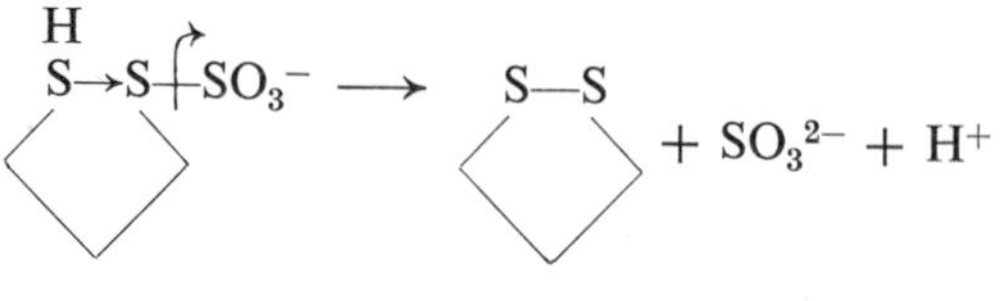

of alkyl thiosulfates are well known. For example, the exchange of sulfite ion with alkyl thiosulfates has been studied in detail.[151]

$$S^*O_3^{2-} \longrightarrow \underset{R}{S{-}SO_3^-} \rightleftharpoons {}^-O_3S^*{-}\underset{R}{S} + SO_3^{2-}$$

CONDENSATIONS

Aldol condensation
Noncatalytic. Formally the aldol condensation can be thought of as the anion of a carbon alpha to a carbonyl group attacking the carbon of

[150] H. Hilz and M. Kittler, *Biochem. Biophys. Res. Commun.* **3**, 140 (1960)
[151] A. Fava and G. Pajaro, *J. Am. Chem. Soc.* **78**, 5203 (1956)

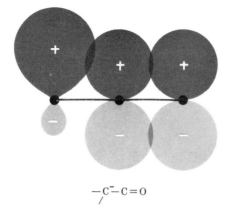

$$-\underset{/}{\overset{}{C^-}}-C=O$$

another carbonyl group. Step I is commonly, but not always, the rate-determining step in nonenzymatic reactions. The ionization of the α-hydrogen will be aided (1) if it is sterically in a favorable position, and (2) if the anion can be stabilized.

$$\overset{\displaystyle O}{\underset{/}{\overset{\backslash H}{C}}-\overset{\|}{C}-} \longrightarrow \overset{\displaystyle O}{\underset{/}{\overset{\backslash}{C^-}}-\overset{\|}{C}-} + H^+ \qquad I$$

$$\underset{O=\overset{|}{C}}{\overset{\backslash}{C^-}} + \overset{|}{\underset{|}{C}}=O \longrightarrow \underset{O=\overset{|}{C}}{\overset{\backslash}{C}}-\overset{|}{\underset{|}{C}}-O^- \qquad II$$

We shall first discuss the steric requirements. Corey and Sneen[152] have found that the α-axial hydrogen of cyclohexanone ionizes about fifty times as fast as the equatorial hydrogen. Resonance in the transition state is aided if the orbital on carbon is parallel to the carbonyl orbitals. This

$$\underset{|}{\overset{H}{\underset{|}{\overset{\backslash}{C^-}}}}-\overset{H^+}{\underset{|}{C}}=O \rightleftharpoons \underset{/}{\overset{H}{\underset{}{\overset{\backslash}{C}}}}=\overset{H^+}{\underset{\backslash}{C}}-O^-$$

means that the carbonyl bond must be perpendicular to the C—H bond that is ionized. To hold these bonds in a perpendicular position to the carbonyl group must be one of the requirements of any enzyme catalyzing an aldol type condensation.

The anion is stabilized by resonance with the carbonyl group. The stability of the anion depends upon how well the oxygen of the carbonyl

[152] E. J. Corey and R. A. Sneen, *J. Am. Chem. Soc.* **78**, 6269 (1956)

group can accommodate a negative charge. The carbonyl of an aldehyde, for example, can accommodate a negative charge much better than the carbonyl of a carboxylate ion. In biological systems these anions may be derived from three sources: (1) aldehydes or ketones, (2) acids or their esters, and (3) glycine.

Aldehydes or ketones. The enzyme aldolase catalyzes the condensation of dihydroxyacetone phosphate with glyceraldehyde-3-phosphate to give fructose-1,6-diphosphate. The enzyme will also catalyze tritium exchange between tritium containing water and dihydroxyacetone phosphate faster than it will catalyze the dealdolization of the fructose-1,6-diphosphate.

$$
\begin{array}{ccc}
CH_2-O-\textcircled{P} & H-C\!\!=\!\!O & \\
| & | & \\
C\!\!=\!\!O & + \quad CHOH & \rightleftharpoons \quad \text{Fructose-1,6-diphosphate} \\
| & | & \\
CH_2OH & CH_2-O-\textcircled{P} &
\end{array}
$$

These results[153] are consistent with a mechanism[154] in which the enzyme catalyzes a rapid enolization of the dihydroxyacetone phosphate followed by the condensation of this anion with the glyceraldehyde-3-phosphate.

This anion must be formed on the enzyme surface in an aldolase-dihydroxyacetone phosphate complex. Evidence for such a complex is obtained from two types of experiments. The aldolase-dihydroxyacetone phosphate may be detected[155] by the appearance of a new absorption band when the substrate and enzyme are mixed. Additional evidence[156] is obtained from exchange reactions of labeled glyceraldehyde-3-phosphate with the C 4,5,6 portion of fructose-1,6-diphosphate in the presence of adolase. Inspection of molecular models will show which of the two hydrogens must be enolized to form fructose-1,6-diphosphate.

Acids. Many biological condensations of carboxylic acids occur: commonly through the enolate ion of the coenzyme A ester. The acyl coenzyme A will form an enolate ion more readily than an oxygen ester,

$$
\left[CH_3-C\!\!\begin{array}{c}O,\\\\O^-,\end{array} \qquad CH_3-C\!\!\begin{array}{c}O^-\\\\O\end{array} \right]
$$

[153] Y. J. Topper, *J. Biol. Chem.* **225**, 419 (1947); B. Bloom and Y. J. Topper, *Science* **124**, 982 (1956); W. J. Rutter and K. H. Ling, *Biochem. et Biophys. Acta* **30**, 71 (1958); I. A. Rose and S. V. Rieder, *J. Biol. Chem.* **231**, 315 (1958)
[154] I. A. Rose and S. V. Rieder, *J. Am. Chem. Soc.* **77**, 5764 (1955)
[155] Y. J. Topper, A. H. Mehler, and B. Bloom, *Science* **126**, 1287 (1957)
[156] I. A. Rose, *Proc. Nat. Acad. Sci. U.S.* **44**, 10 (1958); B. Bloom and Y. J. Topper, *Nature* **181**, 1128 (1958)

such as ethyl acetate, and much more readily than acetate ion. The carbonyl group in acetate ion is unlike the carbonyl group in an aldehyde because of the carboxyl group resonance.

A similar resonance occurs in oxygen esters, but to a much lesser degree. Elements with higher atomic numbers are poor double-bond formers[157] so that a thiol ester would be expected to have even less resonance than oxygen ester. This partially explains the high energy of hydrolysis of

$$
\left[\quad CH_3—C\overset{\displaystyle O}{\underset{\displaystyle OR,}{\Big\langle}} \qquad CH_3—C\overset{\displaystyle O^-}{\underset{\displaystyle _+OR}{\Big\langle}} \quad \right]
$$

acetyl coenzyme A.[158] Because of the hindered ester resonance, the carbonyl group in acetyl coenzyme A is more like an aldehyde than is an oxygen ester, and is more readily available to form an enolate ion. Baker and Harris[159] have shown that the small resonance in thiol esters places a positive charge on the oxygen by accommodating an electron pair in a *d* orbital of sulfur. This effect makes the oxygen even more positive than

$$
CH_3—C\overset{\displaystyle O^+}{\underset{\displaystyle \overset{-}{S}R}{\Big\langle}}
$$

might be expected and certainly must help greatly in forming an enolate ion. Examples[160] of the condensation of the enolate ion of acetyl coenzyme

$$
H_2\overset{\displaystyle H}{\underset{}{C}}{\stackrel{\curvearrowright}{—}}C\overset{\displaystyle \overset{\curvearrowleft}{O}\,{}^{\delta+}}{\underset{\displaystyle SR}{\Big\langle}} \quad \overset{\displaystyle H^+}{\longrightarrow} \quad CH_2{=}C\overset{\displaystyle O^-}{\underset{\displaystyle SR}{\Big\langle}}
$$

A occur in the condensation of acetyl coenzyme A with acetoacetate to form β-hydroxy-β-methylglutaryl CoA, and in the condensation of acetyl coenzyme A with oxalacetic acid to give citric acid.

The latter reaction has been postulated as taking place through the enolate ion[161] of acetyl coenzyme A. However, if the condensing enzyme

[157] K. S. Pitzer, *J. Am. Chem. Soc.* **70**, 2140 (1948)
[158] K. Burton, *Biochem. J.* **59**, 44 (1955)
[159] A. W. Baker and G. H. Harris, *J. Am. Chem. Soc.* **82**, 1923 (1960)
[160] F. Lynen, *Federation Proc.* **12**, 683 (1953); B. K. Pachawat, W. G. Robinson, and M. J. Coon, *J. Biol. Chem.* **216**, 727 (1955)
[161] J. Putter, *Z. physiol. Chem.* **308**, 31 (1957)

and acetyl coenzyme A are dissolved in tritrated water or in D_2O under normal reaction conditions, there is no tritration or deuteration of the acetyl coenzyme A resulting from an enolate ion.[162] Evidently both the oxalacetate and the enzyme are required for enolate ion formation. The oxalacetate anion may function as a basic catalyst aiding in the proton removal. Deuterium studies have also shown that the acetyl coenzyme A reacts with the keto form of oxalacetic acid and not the enol form.[163]

However, there are condensations which occur directly with the acid and not with the coenzyme A ester, such as the condensation of succinic acid with glyoxylic acid to give isocitric acid.[164] The mechanism of this reaction has not been investigated in detail.

Glycine. In many biochemical condensations the anion is derived from glycine.[165] The anion of the amino acid is stabilized by pyridoxal, much as the carbanion is stabilized in the decarboxylation of amino acids by the coenzyme pyridoxal phosphate. In this manner glycine may condense with

[162] A. Marcus and B. Vennesland, *J. Biol. Chem.* **233**, 727 (1958); J. Bove, R. Martin L. Ingraham, and P. K. Stumpf, *J. Biol. Chem.* **234**, 999 (1959)

[163] S. Englard, *J. Biol. Chem.* **234**, 1004 (1959)

[164] E. A. Smith and I. C. Gunsalus, *J. Biol. Chem.* **229**, 305 (1957)

[165] D. E. Metzler, J. B. Longenecker, and E. E. Snell, *J. Am. Chem. Soc.* **75**, 2786 (1953); D. E. Metzler, J. B. Longenecker, and E. E. Snell, *J. Am. Chem. Soc.* **76**, 639 (1954); D. E. Metzler, M. Ikawa, and E. E. Snell, *J. Am. Chem. Soc.* **76**, 648 (1954); A. Karasek and D. M. Greenberg, *J. Biol. Chem.* **227**, 191 (1957)

acetaldehyde to give threonine, or with formaldehyde to give serine. The reverse reactions have been studied in model reactions catalyzed by pyridoxal.

Benzoin type condensations
Two molecules of benzaldehyde condense in the presence of cyanide ion to form benzoin. An anion of the type ϕ—$\overset{\overset{\textstyle O}{\|}}{C}^-$ is required for this condensation. This anion is obtained by the cyanide ion first forming a cyanohydrin with the benzaldehyde. The hydrogen is now labilized by the

$$\phi-\overset{\overset{\textstyle O}{\|}}{C}H + HCN \rightleftharpoons \phi-\overset{\overset{\textstyle H}{|}}{\underset{\underset{\textstyle CN}{|}}{C}}-\overset{\overset{\textstyle O}{|}}{}H$$

cyano group and may ionize to give the cyano addition product of the

$$\phi-\overset{\overset{\textstyle H}{|}}{\underset{\underset{\textstyle CN}{|}}{C}}{}^-\overset{\overset{\textstyle O}{|}}{}$$

required anion. This anion may condense with the carbonyl of a free benzaldehyde and subsequently lose HCN to form benzoin. Thiamine

$$\phi-\overset{\overset{\textstyle H}{\overset{\textstyle O}{|}}}{\underset{\underset{\textstyle CN}{|}}{C}}{}^- + \overset{\overset{\textstyle H}{|}}{\underset{\underset{\textstyle \phi}{|}}{C}}{=}O \longrightarrow \phi-\overset{\overset{\textstyle H}{\overset{\textstyle O}{|}}}{\underset{\underset{\textstyle CN\phi}{|}}{C}}-\overset{\overset{\textstyle H}{|}}{\underset{\underset{\textstyle \phi}{\|}}{C}}-O^- \longrightarrow \phi-\overset{\overset{\textstyle HCN}{+}}{\underset{\underset{\textstyle O}{|}}{C}}-\overset{\overset{\textstyle H}{|}}{\underset{\underset{\textstyle O}{|}}{C}}-\phi$$

catalyzes a similar decondensation and condensation of aldehydes head to head in the transketolase reaction. Xylulose-5-phosphate and ribose-5-phosphate give sedoheptulose-7-phosphate and 3-phosphoglyceric acid. A two-carbon aldehyde is decondensed from the xylulose-5-phosphate and condensed on the ribose-5-phosphate. Breslow has pointed out the similarity of cyanide ion and thiamine both as to structure and mechanism.

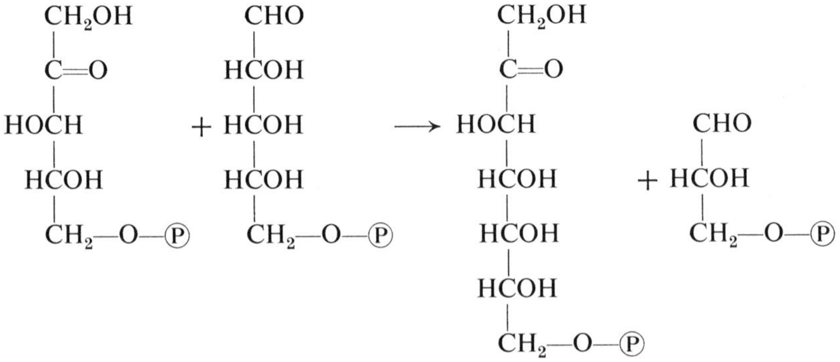

$$
\begin{array}{c}
CH_2OH \\
| \\
C=O \\
| \\
HOCH \\
| \\
HCOH \\
| \\
CH_2-O-\textcircled{P}
\end{array}
\quad + \quad
\begin{array}{c}
CHO \\
| \\
HCOH \\
| \\
HCOH \\
| \\
HCOH \\
| \\
CH_2-O-\textcircled{P}
\end{array}
\quad \longrightarrow \quad
\begin{array}{c}
CH_2OH \\
| \\
C=O \\
| \\
HOCH \\
| \\
HCOH \\
| \\
HCOH \\
| \\
HCOH \\
| \\
CH_2-O-\textcircled{P}
\end{array}
\quad + \quad
\begin{array}{c}
CHO \\
| \\
HCOH \\
| \\
CH_2-O-\textcircled{P}
\end{array}
$$

The reaction very probably proceeds in a mechanism analogous to that of the cyanide ion.[166]

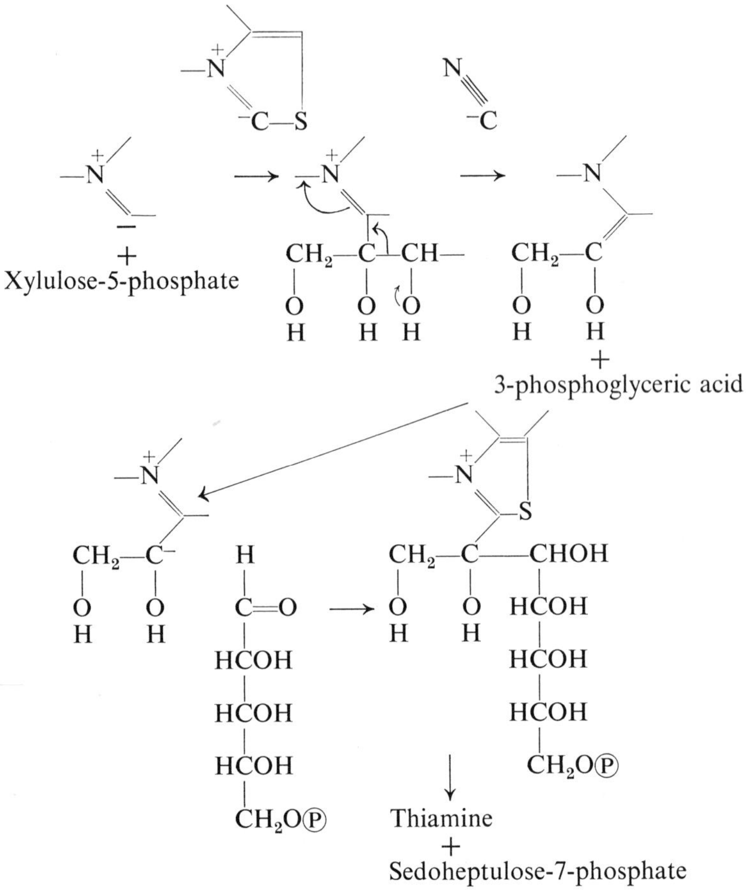

Xylulose-5-phosphate

3-phosphoglyceric acid

Thiamine + Sedoheptulose-7-phosphate

[166] R. Breslow, *J. Am. Chem. Soc.* **80**, 3719 (1958)

The reaction catalyzed by the enzyme phosphoketolase requires thiamine. Phosphoketolase[167] catalyzes the reaction of xylulose with phosphate ion to give acetyl phosphate and glyceraldehyde.

In a mechanism for this reaction, the anion of thiamine condenses with the carbonyl of xylulose and a reverse benzoin condensation occurs as discussed in the transketolase reaction. The resulting intermediate can

$$
\begin{array}{ccc}
\text{—N}^+\text{—S} & \text{—N}^+\text{—S} & \text{—N—S} \\
\left[\begin{array}{l} CH_2OH \\ C=O \\ HOCH \\ HCOH \\ CH_2O\text{—}\textcircled{P} \end{array}\right] \longrightarrow &
\begin{array}{l} CH_2\text{—C—CH—OH} \\ \quad O \quad O \; HCOH \\ \quad H \quad H \\ \quad\quad CH_2\text{—O—}\textcircled{P} \end{array} \longrightarrow &
\begin{array}{l} CH_2\text{—C} \quad + \; CHO \\ \quad O \quad O \quad\quad CHOH \\ \quad H \quad H \quad\quad CH_2\text{—O—}\textcircled{P} \end{array}
\end{array}
$$

then lose a hydroxyl group in a manner rather analogous to the serine-to-pyruvic-acid mechanism catalyzed by pyridoxal. Ketonization of this enol

$$
\begin{array}{ccc}
\text{N—S} & \text{—N}^+\text{—S} & \text{—N}^+\text{—S} \\
\begin{array}{l} CH_2\text{—C} \\ \; O \quad O \\ \; H \quad H \end{array} \longrightarrow &
\begin{array}{l} CH_2=C \\ \quad O \\ \quad H \end{array} \longrightarrow &
\begin{array}{l} CH_3\text{—C} \\ \quad\quad O \end{array}
\end{array}
$$

would give 2-acetylthiamine. 2-Acetylthiamine probably has a high free energy of hydrolysis. The hydrolysis products would be acetic acid and thiamine. Two factors allow this prediction: (1) ester resonance is not possible, and (2) there must be a very strong repulsion between the positive nitrogen and the carbonyl dipole. Although the free energy of hydrolysis has not been measured, two model compounds, 2-acetyl-3-benzyl-4-methyl-thiazolium iodide and 2-benzoyl-3,4-dimethylthiazolium iodide, have been found to be very active acylating agents.[168] If 2-acetylthiamine has a high free energy of hydrolysis, it would be expected to exchange thiamine for

[167] E. C. Heath, J. Hurwitz, B. L. Horecker, and A. Ginsburg, *J. Biol. Chem.* **231**, 1009 (1958)

[168] R. Breslow and E. McNelis, *J. Am. Chem. Soc.* **82**, 2394 (1960); F. G. White and L. L. Ingraham, *J. Am. Chem. Soc.* **82**, 4114 (1960)

phosphate ion and give acetyl phosphate by the nucleophilic attack of phosphate ion on the carbonyl group.

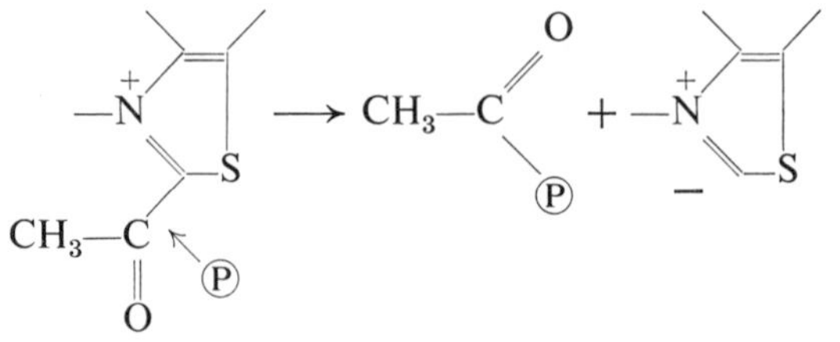

$$\text{—} \overset{+}{\text{N}} \underset{\text{S}}{\text{—}} \quad \underset{\overset{\parallel}{\text{O}}}{\overset{\text{CH}_3\text{—C}}{\underset{\text{(P)}}{}}} \longrightarrow \text{CH}_3\text{—C} \overset{\text{O}}{\underset{\text{(P)}}{}} + \text{—} \overset{+}{\text{N}} \underset{\text{—S}}{\text{—}}$$

ALKYLATION REACTIONS

Amines and phenols

Alkylation reactions occur by two general mechanisms. Nucleophiles, such as phenols, alcohols, and amines, are commonly alkylated by nucleophilic displacement reaction, whereas olefins and aromatic compounds are alkylated by electrophilic attack of a carbonium ion.

The important factor in the alkylation of phenols, alcohols, or amines is that the alkyl group is attached to an easily replaceable group so that a nucleophilic displacement reaction can occur. Examples of methylating agents used in nonenzymic reactions are dimethyl sulfate and methyl

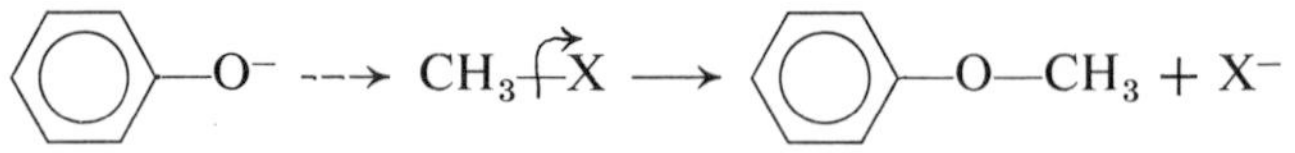

$$\langle\bigcirc\rangle\text{—O}^- \text{ ---> } \text{CH}_3\overset{\curvearrowright}{\text{—}}\text{X} \longrightarrow \langle\bigcirc\rangle\text{—O—CH}_3 + \text{X}^-$$

iodide. Sulfate ion and iodide ion are both easily displaced groups. The biological methylating agent is S-adenosylmethionine. This compound is formed by the reaction of methionine with adenosine triphosphate. The sulfonium ion makes an easily replaceable group because it will accommodate a pair of electrons on leaving to form a thio ether. This reagent will enzymically methylate[169] many phenols and catechols.

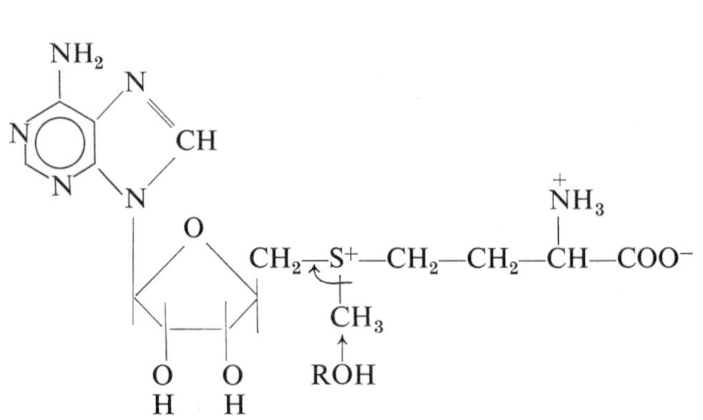

Sulfonium compounds will also act as alkylating agents in nonenzymic reactions.[170] Interestingly, the sulfonium compounds alkylate at a rate

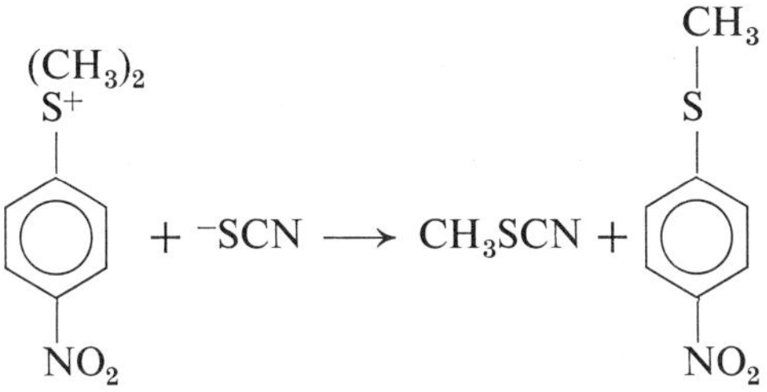

$$
\begin{array}{c}
(CH_3)_2 \\
S^+ \\
\end{array}
\underset{NO_2}{\bigcirc}
+ \; ^-SCN \longrightarrow CH_3SCN +
\begin{array}{c}
CH_3 \\
| \\
S \\
\end{array}
\underset{NO_2}{\bigcirc}
$$

over 3500 times as fast as the corresponding ammonium compound,

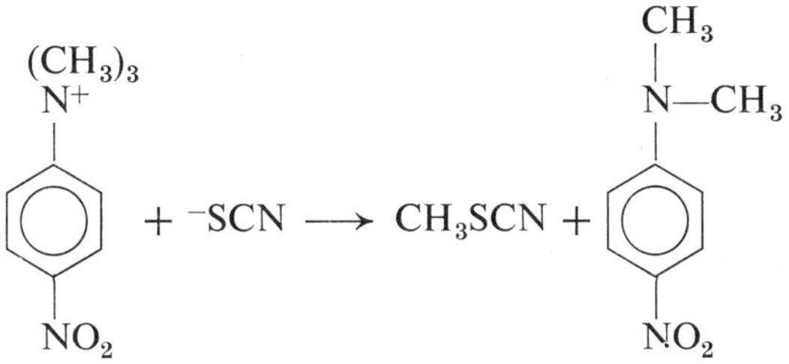

$$
\begin{array}{c}
(CH_3)_3 \\
N^+ \\
\end{array}
\underset{NO_2}{\bigcirc}
+ \; ^-SCN \longrightarrow CH_3SCN +
\begin{array}{c}
CH_3 \\
| \\
N-CH_3 \\
\end{array}
\underset{NO_2}{\bigcirc}
$$

probably because the C—S bond is a much more polarizable bond than the C—N bond, and therefore the activation energy is lower.

Olefins

Alkylation of olefins or aromatic compounds occurs by the attack of a carbonium ion of the alkylating agent on the olefin or aromatic. A good example is the Friedel-Crafts reaction. An example closer to biochemistry is the ring alkylation of phenol by benzyldiphenyl phosphate.[171] Presumably

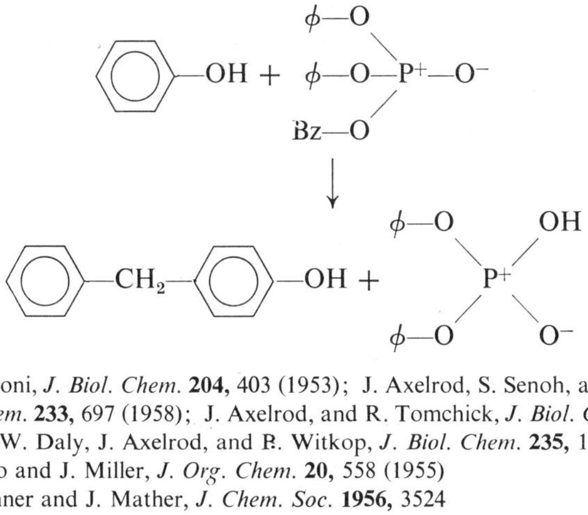

$$
\bigcirc\!\!\!-OH + \begin{array}{c} \phi-O \\ \phi-O-P^+-O^- \\ Bz-O \end{array}
$$

$$
\downarrow
$$

$$
\bigcirc\!\!\!-CH_2-\bigcirc\!\!\!-OH + \begin{array}{c} \phi-O \quad OH \\ P^+ \\ \phi-O \quad O^- \end{array}
$$

[169] G. L. Cantoni, *J. Biol. Chem.* **204**, 403 (1953); J. Axelrod, S. Senoh, and B. Witkop, *J. Biol. Chem.* **233**, 697 (1958); J. Axelrod, and R. Tomchick, *J. Biol. Chem.* **233**, 702 (1958); J. W. Daly, J. Axelrod, and B. Witkop, *J. Biol. Chem.* **235**, 1155 (1959)

[170] B. A. Bolto and J. Miller, *J. Org. Chem.* **20**, 558 (1955)

[171] G. W. Kenner and J. Mather, *J. Chem. Soc.* **1956**, 3524

the benzyldiphenyl phosphate ionizes to give a benzyl carbonium ion which alkylates the phenol.

A very similar enzymic reaction is the dimerization of isopentenyl phosphate in the formation of squalene from mevalonic acid. In this reaction a primary carbonium ion or something very close to this must be produced. This is helped somewhat by having the better than usual

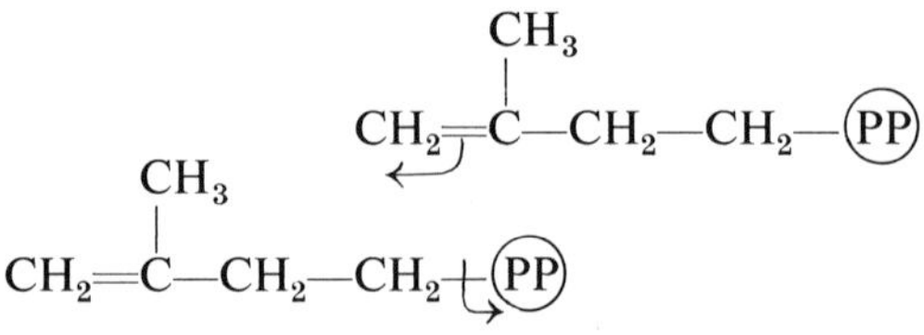

$$CH_2\!\!=\!\!\overset{\overset{\displaystyle CH_3}{|}}{C}\!\!-\!\!CH_2\!\!-\!\!CH_2\!\!-\!\!\boxed{PP}$$

$$CH_2\!\!=\!\!\overset{\overset{\displaystyle CH_3}{|}}{C}\!\!-\!\!CH_2\!\!-\!\!CH_2\!\!-\!\!\boxed{PP}$$

leaving group, the pyrophosphate ion. The olefin may be held so close to the phosphate on the enzyme surface that the primary carbonium exists for only a very short time.

REARRANGEMENTS

Hydrogen shifts of glycols

The rearrangement of a 1,2-glycol to a ketone may proceed either by hydride shift or by a dehydration to the enol. This type of reaction is

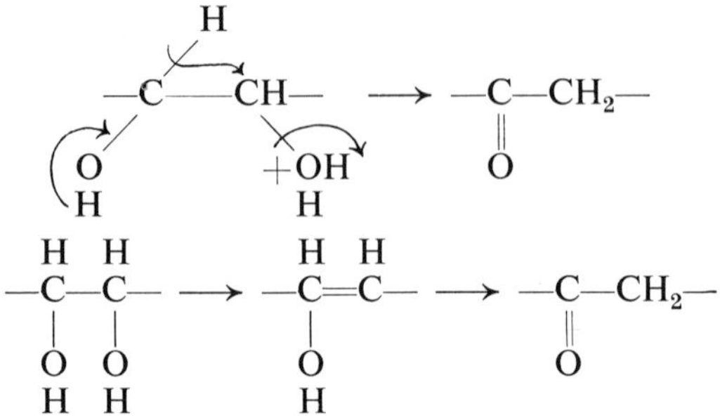

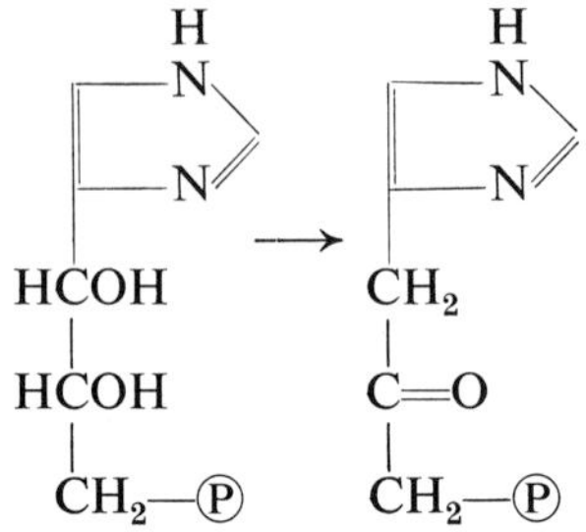

[172] B. N. Ames, *J. Biol. Chem.* **228**, 131 (1957)

known in biochemistry but the mechanism is not known. The enzyme imidazole glycerol phosphate dehydrogenase[172] will catalyze the rearrangement of D-erythro imidazole glycerol phosphate to imidazol acetol phosphate.

Hydrogen shifts in α-hydroxy ketones

The rearrangement of a α-hydroxy carbonyl compound may occur by

$$
\begin{array}{ccc}
\text{C=O} & & \text{H—C—OH} \\
| & \rightleftharpoons & | \\
\text{HCOH} & & \text{C=O} \\
| & & |
\end{array}
$$

two mechanisms. The first mechanism is that of a direct hydride transfer.

$$
\begin{array}{ccc}
\overset{\text{H}}{\underset{\text{O} \quad \text{O}}{-C\!-\!C-}} & \rightarrow & \overset{\text{H} \quad \text{H}}{\underset{^+\text{O} \quad \text{OH}}{-C\!-\!C-}} \rightarrow \overset{\text{H} \quad \text{H}}{\underset{\text{O} \quad \text{O}}{-C\!-\!C-}} + \text{H}^+
\end{array}
$$

The second type of mechanism proceeds through an enediol intermediate, the hydrogen ion being lost and picked up again from solution. If this

$$
\begin{array}{ccc}
\overset{\text{H}}{\underset{\underset{\text{H}}{\text{O}} \quad \underset{}{\text{O}}}{-C\!-\!C-}} & \rightarrow & \underset{\underset{\text{H}}{\text{O}} \quad \underset{\text{H}}{\text{O}}}{-C\!=\!C-} \rightarrow \overset{\text{H}}{\underset{\underset{}{\text{O}} \quad \underset{\text{H}}{\text{O}}}{-C\!-\!C-}}
\end{array}
$$

occurs, the product formed in D_2O solvent will contain deuterium. This has been found to be true for the isomerization of fructose-6-phosphate to glucose-6-phosphate, and also for the triosephosphate isomerase-catalyzed isomerization of the dihydroxyacetone phosphate to glyceraldehyde-3-phosphate.[173]

Hydrogen shifts in α-keto aldehydes

α-keto aldehydes will rearrange in a similar type of reaction to α-hydroxy acids. For example, glyoxal will rearrange in basic solution to glycollic

[173] Y. J. Topper, *J. Biol. Chem.* **225,** 419 (1957); B. Bloom and Y. J. Topper, *Science* **124,** 982 (1956); S. V. Rieder and I. A. Rose, *J. Biol. Chem.* **234,** 1007 (1959)

acid. Reaction in D_2O produces glycollic acid with no nonexchangeable deuterium.[174] This result is consistent with a hydride ion rearrangement. Similarily, the rearrangement of phenyl glyoxal to mandelic acid in D_2O produces mandelic acid with no nonexchangeable deuterium.[175] In this example either the phenyl group or a hydrogen may migrate with a pair of

$$
\begin{array}{ccc}
\text{H} \quad \text{H} \quad ^-\text{OD} & \text{H} \quad \text{H} & \text{H} \quad \text{OD} \\
\text{C---C} & \longrightarrow & \text{C--C---OD} \longrightarrow \text{H---C--C} \\
\text{O} \qquad \text{O} & \text{O} \quad \text{O} & ^-\text{O} \qquad \text{O}
\end{array}
$$

$$
\downarrow
$$

$$
\text{DO---CH}_2\text{---C} \overset{\text{O}}{\underset{\text{O}^-}{}}
$$

electrons. Carbon 14 labeling has shown that the carbon skeleton does not change and therefore that a phenyl group does not migrate. The mechanism for phenyl glyoxal must be therefore the same as that for glyoxal. This reaction requires essentially two agents: the nucleophile to attack the

$$
\begin{array}{ccc}
\text{H} \quad \overline{\text{O}}\text{H} & \text{H} & \text{OH} \\
\phi\text{---C--C} & \longrightarrow \phi\text{---C--C---OH} & \longrightarrow \phi\text{---C--C} \\
\text{O} \qquad \text{O} \quad \text{I} & \text{O} \quad \text{O}^- \quad \text{II} & ^-\text{O} \qquad \text{O}
\end{array}
$$

carboxyl in the first reaction, and a base to keep the $-O^-$ ionized for the second reaction. Franzen[176] has designed a catalyst for this, in which the nucleophile is a sulfhydryl group and the base is an amino group. These catalysts are the N,N-dialkyl-β-aminoethylmercaptans, and will catalyze the reaction of phenyl glyoxal to mandelic acid at physiological pH values. Reaction in D_2O will produce mandelic acid containing no deuterium, which indicates that the hydrogen which shifted never left the compound. In methanol the product of the reaction is methyl mandelate.[176]   These

[174] Friedenhagen and Bonhoffer, *Z. physik Chem. (Leipzig)* A**181**, 379 (1938)

[175] W. v. E. Doering, T. I. Taylor, and E. F. Schoenewaldt, *J. Am. Chem. Soc.* **70**, 455 (1948)

[176] V. Franzen, *Ber. deut. chem. Ges.* **88**, 1361 (1955)

observations are all consistent with the following mechanism:

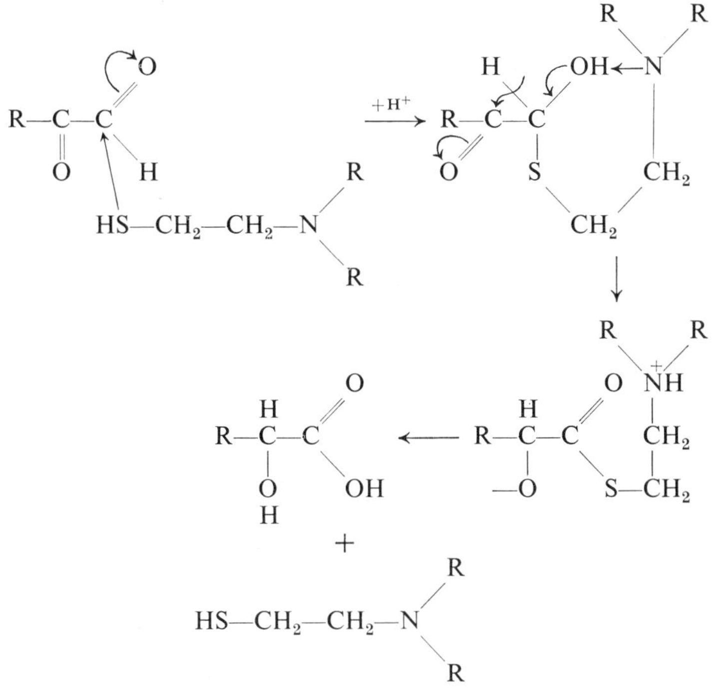

The N,N-diethyl-β-aminoethylmercaptan has a turnover number of 0.7 at 20° in methanol, which is increased to 6.7 in β-piperidylethylmercaptan. These turnover numbers are still quite insignificant compared to the

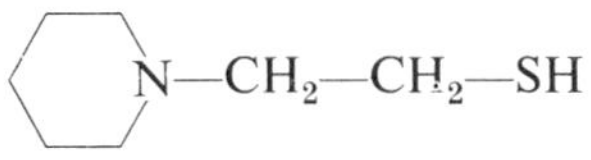

turnover number for glyoxylase I of 35,000.

Glyoxylase I catalyzes the reaction between methyl glyoxal and gluta-thione to give the glutathione ester of lactic acid. Reaction in D_2O produces lactic acid containing no deuterium[177] in agreement with the model system. Presumably the mercaptan group is furnished by the glutathione and the amino group by the enzyme. However, the enzyme must be doing something more than the model system because of the great discrepancy in the turnover numbers.

[177] V. Franzen, *Ber. deut. chem. Ges.* **89**, 1020 (1956)

Rearrangements catalyzed by B_{12}

Enzymes containing vitamin B_{12} catalyze two very interesting rearrangements. One of these is the rearrangement of glutamic acid to β-methylaspartic acid.[178] Although the mechanism for this reaction is unknown,

$$\begin{array}{ccc}
^1COO^- & & ^1COO^- \\
| & & | \\
^2HC{-}NH_3^+ & & ^2HC{-}NH_3^+ \\
| & & | \\
^3CH_2 & \longrightarrow & ^4CH \\
| & & \diagup \quad \diagdown \\
^4CH_2 & & ^3CH_3 \quad ^5COOH \\
| & & \\
^5COOH & &
\end{array}$$

an almost plausible carbanion mechanism can be postulated. Labeling experiments show that carbon 3 of glutamic acid becomes the methyl group of β-methylaspartic acid, carbon 4 becomes the tertiary carbon, and carbon 5 remains a carboxyl.

The positive charge of the cobalt in the vitamin B_{12} could help to stabilize a carbanion. This carbanion could undergo an internal nucleophilic displacement reaction to displace the ammonia. If this cyclopropane

$$\begin{array}{ccccc}
COO^- & & COO^- & & COO^- \\
| & & | & & | \\
HC{-}NH_3^+ & & HC{+}NH_3^+ & & CH \\
| & & | & & | \diagup \\
CH_2 & \longrightarrow & CH_2 & \longrightarrow & CH \quad\quad + NH_3 \\
| & & | & & | \diagdown \\
CH_2 & & {}^-CH & & CH_2 \\
| & & | & & | \\
COOH & & COOH & & COOH
\end{array}$$

ring opened between carbons 2 and 3 with attack by the enzyme, and the ammonia then displaced the enzyme, the product β-methylaspartic acid would be formed. The attack by the enzyme is necessary because the experimental facts are that L-glutamic acid rearranges to L-β-methylaspartic acid. Direct displacement on the cyclopropane ring by ammonia would cause inversion.

A similar reaction is the rearrangement[179] of methylmalonyl coenzyme A to give succinyl coenzyme A. A similar mechanism[180] may be written.

[178] H. A. Barker, H. Weissbach, and R. D. Smyth, *Proc. Nat. Acad. Sci. U.S.* **44**, 1093 (1958)

[179] W. S. Beck and S. Ochoa, *J. Biol. Chem.* **232**, 931 (1958)

[180] This mechanism was suggested by H. J. Bright in a private conversation

$$
\begin{array}{ccc}
\text{COOH} & \text{COOH} & \text{COOH} \\
| & | & | \\
\text{E}{\rightarrow}\text{HC} & \text{E—CH} & \text{E}\!\!-\!\!\text{CH}{\leftarrow}\text{NH}_3 \\
| & | & | \\
\quad\text{CH}_2 \longrightarrow & \text{HC—CH}_2{}^- \xrightarrow{+\text{H}^+} & \text{HC—CH}_3 \\
| & | & | \\
\text{HC} & \text{COOH} & \text{COOH} \\
| & & \downarrow \\
\text{COOH} & & \text{COO}^- \\
& & | \\
& & \text{CH—NH}_3{}^+ \\
& & | \\
& & \text{CH—CH}_3 \\
& & | \\
& & \text{COOH}
\end{array}
$$

Again the carbanion would be stabilized by the positive charge on the cobalt of the vitamin B_{12}. The difficulty with both of these carbanion

$$
\begin{array}{ccc}
\text{COO}^- & \text{COO}^- & \text{COO}^- \\
| & | & | \\
\text{CH}_2 & {}^-\text{CH} & \text{CH} \\
| & | & \quad\backslash \\
\text{CH}_2 \longrightarrow & \text{CH}_2 \longrightarrow & \quad\text{CH}_2 \longrightarrow \\
| & | & | \\
\text{COSCoA} & \text{COSCoA} & \text{C} \\
& & \quad\quad | \\
& & \text{HO}\quad\text{S} \\
& & \quad\text{CoA}
\end{array}
$$

$$
\begin{array}{cc}
\text{COO}^- & \text{COO}^- \\
| & | \\
\text{CH—CH}_2{}^- \xrightarrow{+\text{H}^+} & \text{CH—CH}_3 \\
| & | \\
\text{COSCoA} & \text{COSCoA}
\end{array}
$$

reactions is the primary carbanion formed in the rearrangement. This carbanion can not be stabilized by enolate formation so that the mechanism is only possible if the cobalt can stabilize the carbanion.

If these reaction mechanisms are correct, then B_{12} could be considered as a biological Grignard reagent. Grignard reagents merely provide a way to stabilize carbanions. Interesting, Grignard reagents are used as a common method to reduce compounds to the hydrocarbon, and vitamin B_{12} is essential for synthesis of desoxy ribose.[181]

Lynen and others have suggested that the β-methylmalonyl CoA–succinyl CoA arrangement may be a free radical reaction.[182] The methylmalonyl

[181] L. A. Manson, *J. Biol. Chem.* **235**, 2955 (1960)
[182] H. Eggerer, P. Overath, F. Lynen, and E. R. Stadtman, *J. Am. Chem. Soc.* **82**, 2643 (1960)

CoA could be oxidized to a radical by cobaltic ion, the radical rearranges, and the resulting radical is reduced to succinic acid.

$$\underset{\underset{\text{COSCoA}}{|}}{\overset{\overset{\text{COOH}}{|}}{HC}}-CH_3 + Co^{3+} \longrightarrow \underset{\underset{\text{COOH}}{|}}{\overset{\overset{\text{COOH}}{|}}{HC}}-CH_2\cdot + Co^{2+} + H^+$$

$$\underset{\underset{\text{COSCoA}}{|}}{\overset{\overset{\text{COOH}}{|}}{HC}}-CH_2\cdot \longrightarrow \cdot\underset{\underset{\text{COSCoA}}{|}}{\overset{\overset{\text{COOH}}{|}}{CH}}-CH_2$$

$$\cdot\underset{\underset{\text{COSCoA}}{|}}{\overset{\overset{\text{COOH}}{|}}{CH}}-CH_2 + Co^{2+} + H^+ \longrightarrow \underset{\underset{\underset{\text{COSCoA}}{|}}{\overset{\text{CH}_2}{|}}}{\overset{\overset{\text{COOH}}{|}}{CH_2}}$$

The oxidation of benzaldehyde to benzoyl radical by cobaltic ion[183] has

$$Co^{3+} + \phi CHO \longrightarrow \phi CO + Co^{2+} + H^+$$

been cited as an example of oxidation of organic molecules to radicals by cobaltic ion. However, the oxidation of benzaldehyde must be very different from oxidation of a methyl group.

MISCELLANEOUS REACTIONS

Racemization of amino acids[184]

The Schiff base formed between pyridoxal and an amino acid will undergo reactions requiring stabilization of an anion other than decarboxylations and eliminations. A proton may be readily lost from the α-carbon atom because the electron pair is placed on the quaternary nitrogen as in decarboxations. The proton may be added back again equally well to either side of the planar carbon so that racemization will occur.

[183] A. F. Trotman-Dickenson, *Free Radicals*, John Wiley and Sons, New York (1959) p. 10

[184] J. Olivard, D. E. Metzler, and E. E. Snell, *J. Biol. Chem.* **199**, 669 (1952); D. E. Metzler, M. Ikawa, and E. E. Snell, *J. Am. Chem. Soc.* **76**, 648 (1954)

$$R—\overset{\overset{\displaystyle H}{|}}{\underset{\underset{\displaystyle CH}{||}}{C}}—COOH \qquad R—\overset{\overset{\displaystyle }{||}}{\underset{\underset{\displaystyle CH}{||}}{C}}—COOH \qquad + \; H^+$$

Transamination[185]

If the proton is added back to the —CH= group and then hydrolysis occurs, the products will be the α-keto acid and pyridoxime. The reverse reaction of the pyridoxime with another α-keto acid will cause transamination.

$$R—\overset{\overset{N}{||}}{\underset{\underset{CH}{|}}{C}}—COOH \;\overset{+H^+}{\underset{-H_+}{\rightleftarrows}}\; R—\overset{\overset{N}{||}}{\underset{\underset{CH_2}{|}}{C}}—COOH \;\overset{+H_2O}{\underset{-H_2O}{\rightleftarrows}}\; \overset{\overset{NH_2}{|}}{\underset{\underset{CH_2}{|}}{}} \;+\; R—\overset{}{\underset{\underset{O}{||}}{C}}—COOH$$

Summary and conclusions

Enzyme-catalyzed reactions obey the fundamental rules of chemical reactions. For this reason, a knowledge of orbitals and certain basic mechanisms is invaluable to the enzyme chemist in understanding the action of enzymes.

Nucleophilic and electrophilic displacements are fundamental reactions important to the understanding of any reaction mechanisms. Displacement reactions require a specific stereochemistry and therefore that the attacking groups must be in the proper position in relation to the substrate. Often a double displacement reaction is more efficient than two single displacement reactions.

Often the function of an enzyme or a coenzyme is merely to act as an acid or a base, *i.e.*, to stabilize either a positive or negative charge. Metals, thiamine, pyridoxal, pyridine nucleotides, vitamin B_{12}, and even the protein itself, among others, may serve this purpose.

[185] D. E Metzler, J. Olivard, and E. E. Snell, *J. Am. Chem. Soc.* **76,** 644 (1954)

Metals act not only as acid catalysts but also to stabilize free radicals, and also in certain other specialized chemical functions such as carrying oxygen. Metals may undergo oxidation-reduction reactions much faster when chelated in a biological system than in free solution because of the Franck-Condon principle. Ligand field theory is an important factor in biological metal-catalyzed reactions. This theory explains why metals in biological systems may behave so differently from metals in the usual inorganic compounds.

Finally the functions of the protein should not be overlooked. The protein probably serves primarily to hold catalytic groups or the substrate in the proper position. Homoallyl conjugation, allyl radicals, and enolate ions all require that the substrate be held in a specific position. Special holding functions of the protein are also required for the stereochemistry required in displacement reactions, and to produce fields around metallic ions as predicted by ligand field theory.

index

105